KS2

Success

Workbook

Lynn Huggins-Cooper

English

Contents

Reading

Writing

Test practice

Answers

See additional answer booklet

Research

Research for an article

Carry out some research on extreme sports – and write a magazine article.

Research for a leaflet

Research into entertainment facilities for kids near you – and create a leaflet.

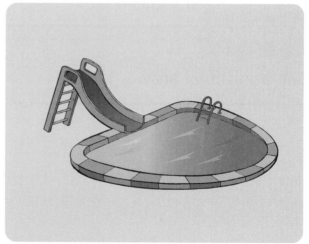

Research for a web page

Find out about your favourite animal – and build a free web page!

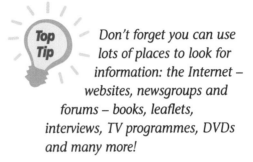

Top Tip *Don't forget you can use lots of places to look for information: the Internet – websites, newsgroups and forums – books, leaflets, interviews, TV programmes, DVDs and many more!*

Research for a report

Do some research on your favourite computer game. Are there any clubs or 'cheat' sites on the Internet about your game? Write a report on it.

I'm going to the climbing wall to find out more!

Is that research – or just good fun?

The language of books

The words used with books

Answer these questions.

1 What is an ISBN number?

_____

2 What is it used for?

_____

3 Whereabouts on a book would you find it?

_____

4 What is blurb?

_____

5 What does an author do?

_____

6 What does an illustrator do?

_____

More terms

Now answer these questions.

1 What is an appendix used for? What would you find in an appendix?

_____

_____

2 What is a glossary used for?

_____

3 Can you describe what is meant by non-fiction?

_____

4 Can you describe what fiction means?

_____

5 What is an index?

_____

6 What are footnotes and whereabouts would you find them?

_____

Parenthesis 1

Fill in the missing words using the words in the box below:

> brackets   afterthoughts   parenthesis   information   interruptions   writing

Parenthesis means words that are added in **1** _____

to a piece of **2** _____ to give us more

3 _____. Sometimes the words in

4 _____ are explanations. Brackets can also be used to add

5 _____ and **6** _____.

Parenthesis 2

Look at these examples of words used in parenthesis and decide whether they are explanations or afterthoughts. Mark explanations with E and afterthoughts with A.

1 The boy (who had already been to the cinema)
    said that the film was hilarious. ☐

2 The cat (who had hidden a mouse under the cushion)
    looked smug. ☐

3 I will be on the school team this year (I hope!). ☐

4 The teacher (who already looked furious) threatened that
    he would get cross if anyone else spoke. ☐

5 'I love toffees!' she said (and grabbed a huge fistful). ☐

Isn't a glossary the stuff girls put on their lips?

No, silly! If you don't know what it means, look it up in the glossary!

Description and imagery

Write your own similes

Write a simile for each of these objects.

1 sea _____

2 sun _____

3 cat _____

4 worm _____

5 spider _____

6 bat _____

Top Tip *Remember, a metaphor is when something is described as something else; a simile is when it is described as **like** something else.*

Sam is as stinky as manure!

And Mel is as mean as a rattlesnake!

Write your own metaphors

Write a metaphor for each of these things.

1 baby's skin   _____

2 strawberry   _____

3 ladybird   _____

4 ice cube   _____

5 grass   _____

6 moonlight   _____

Personification

Match the personification description to the correct word.

1 Autumn

> is a chubby little boy, dressed in green. His moods change from the temper of the blustering wind to the warmth of a sunny smile in minutes!

2 Snow

> is a woman with copper hair and a dress made from leaves.

> is a beautiful lady dressed in diamonds and white fur.

3 Spring

Top Tip   *Read lots of poetry to find examples of personification, metaphors and similes.*

Alliteration and onomatopoeia

Find the alliteration

Underline the words that alliterate in each sentence.

1   Slimy slugs slide across the path.

2   Pink pigs prefer to eat potatoes.

3   Dreadful, dangerous dragons breathe flames.

4   Ghastly, gruesome ghouls groan in haunted castles.

5   Cheeky chipmunks chirrup at the birds as they steal their nuts.

Think up words

Think of words that alliterate with 'sun' and 'moon'. Write them in the shapes.

Match the words

Match the words that alliterate – and make the most sense!

1 slimy   girls

2 sizzling   foxes

3 furry   slugs

4 sparkling   sausages

5 giggling   sea

Top Tip
You often find examples of alliteration in the titles of books or films – look out for examples!

Find the onomatopoeia

Circle the words that are onomatopoeic.

pop

come

slurp

leg

smash

wobble

crash

table

cat

I can use alliteration better than my swotty sister!

No you can't, you bothersome, beastly brother!

Special words

Idioms

Use the words in the box below to complete the idioms:

finger   biscuit   hot   weather

1 He is feeling under the _____.

2 She can wrap her grandad around her little _____.

3 That man is always blowing _____ and cold.

4 You really take the _____!

Explain the idiom

Explain the meaning of each idiom.

1 Under the weather. _____

_____

2 Taking the biscuit. _____

_____

3 Blowing hot and cold. _____

_____

4 Keep your hair on! _____

_____

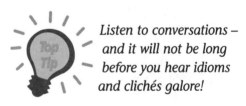

Listen to conversations – and it will not be long before you hear idioms and clichés galore!

Matching proverbs

Match the beginnings and endings of these proverbs.

1 A stitch in time   is worth two in the bush.

2 Too many cooks   saves nine.

3 A bird in the hand   spoil the broth.

What proverbs mean

Explain what these proverbs mean.

1 A stitch in time saves nine.

_____

_____

2 Too many cooks spoil the broth.

_____

_____

3 A bird in the hand is worth two in the bush.

_____

_____

Clichés

Match the beginnings and endings of these clichés.

1 It's raining   the day.

2 At the end of   a parrot.

3 Starting on a   cats and dogs.

4 As sick as   level playing field.

Ambiguity

Spot the real meaning!

Read these sentences. What do you think the writer means in each case?

1 The dog chased the cat, because it was bored. (Which animal was bored? Was the dog trying to cheer the cat up, because she was bored, or was the dog looking for mischief because he was bored?)

_____

2 If that dog doesn't want his dinner, throw it away!

_____

3 The mother scolded the girl, because she was being nasty.

_____

Making sense

Fill in the missing words using the words in the box below:

> ambiguous   clear   sentences   unclear   pronouns

If the meaning of a sentence is **1** _____, it is

2 _____. Sometimes, **3** _____ are ambiguous,

because the **4** _____ such as he and she are badly placed. It is

important to make your meaning **5** _____.

Imagine if you said, 'If that cat doesn't want her food, throw it away,' and your mum threw the cat in the bin!

Make it clear!

Rewrite the sentences to make the meaning clear.

1 The fox ate the rabbit, because it was hungry.

_____

2 The man frowned at the boy, because he was fierce.

_____

3 The woman picked up the dog, because she was lost.

_____

Using the words

Answer these questions.

1 What do people mean when they say that a sentence is ambiguous?

_____

_____

2 Why is it important to make your meaning clear?

_____

3 Which type of word can make a sentence ambiguous if you are not careful?

_____

More on making it clear!

Rewrite these sentences to make the meaning clear.

1 The monkey chased the butterfly, because it was beautiful.

_____

2 Shushi decided that the dog's collar was too big, so she sold it.

_____

3 The leak was repaired before much damage could be done by the man.

_____

4 The shark ate the fish, because it was huge.

_____

Top Tip *Sometimes, meaning becomes unclear, because the sentence you are writing goes on and on... It is better to use shorter sentences to make your meaning clear. Be careful where you put pronouns, too!*

School? I'm ambiguous about it...

I don't think the headteacher is ambiguous about you!

Reading investigation

Build a bookbug!

You are going to make an ever-growing bookbug about the books you read.

It will make a great display for your bedroom wall, or you could ask your mum or dad if you can put it up in the kitchen!

What to do

Make a head for your bug out of paper scraps, sweet wrappers and card. Be as imaginative as possible. You could make it look like a caterpillar or a worm, or even an alien!

Make the head about the size of a cereal packet. If you are feeling very arty, you can make a 3D head by using boxes and packages – but don't make it too heavy, or you will not be able to attach it to the wall.

If you use cardboard packaging, take the boxes apart and turn them inside out before using them – plain card is easier to paint.

Every time you read a book, make another segment for your bookbug. You could stick on sequins, beads, feathers – in fact, anything you think of – round the edges.

Top Tip *See how long you can make your bookbug. You could even ask friends and family members to add their own reviews.*

Fiction segment

If the book you have read is fiction, include this information in the segment.

- Title of book:
- Author:
- Illustrator (if applicable):
- Favourite characters:
- Main problem or issue:
- Was there a message in the story?
- Was there a twist in the tail?

Non-fiction segment

If the book you have read is non-fiction, include this information in the segment.

- Title of book:
- Author:
- Illustrator (if applicable):
- How much information did you learn from this book?
- How easy was it to find the information you wanted?
- Was there a glossary?
- How hard/easy was the book to read?

Contractions

Missing words

Fill in the missing words using the words in the box below:

> friends   apostrophe   missed   speaking
>
> letters   formal   informal

Contractions are words that have **1** _____ missing.

An **2** _____ shows where the letters have been **3** _____

out. Words like this are used in **4** _____ writing, such as:

- Letters to **5** _____

- When a character in a story is **6** _____

Contractions are not used in pieces of **7** _____ writing, such as

reports or business letters.

Contractions in full

Write these contractions in their full form. For example: *I've* becomes *I have*.

1 won't _____   **4** they're _____

2 can't _____   **5** don't _____

3 you've _____   **6** she'll _____

Matching contractions

Match these words to their contractions.

1 I cannot   don't

2 I am   I'd

3 I have   I can't

4 we are   I'd

5 do not   I've

6 I had   we're

7 I would   I'm

Remember, contractions can be used in informal writing, like letters to friends. They should not be used for formal work.

Shorten the words

Rewrite these sentences, using contractions wherever possible.

1 The boys would not go to bed.

_____

2 I will not be able to come to the party.

_____

3 We are going out now.

_____

4 You have got to be quiet!

_____

5 I am going to the shops now.

_____

Take away the contractions

Rewrite these sentences so that they do not contain contractions.

1 I can't do it!

_____

2 I wouldn't like to go anywhere cold.

_____

3 No it's not!

_____

4 It doesn't matter.

_____

5 I've got a huge bowl of sweets.

_____

So a contraction is where letters are missing?

Like the ones you never write back to your pen pal?

Apostrophes

Apostrophe + s

Rewrite these phrases to add a possessive apostrophe. For example: *The bowl that belongs to the cat* becomes *The cat's bowl.*

1 The ball that belongs to the baby   _____

2 The hat that belongs to the man   _____

3 The coat that belongs to the girl   _____

4 The bag of sweets that belongs to
   the teacher   _____

5 The collar that belongs to the dog   _____

Words that already end with s

When a word already ends in -s, the apostrophe is sometimes added without adding another -s. For example: *The sister belonging to James* becomes *James' sister*. This is called the possessive apostrophe.

Rewrite these sentences adding a possessive apostrophe.

1 The cats paws were pink.   _____

2 The ladies hats were all huge. _____

3 The girls bikes were new.   _____

4 The boys trousers were all blue. _____

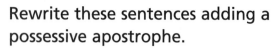

More possessive apostrophes

Rewrite these phrases, putting in the possessive apostrophes.

1 The favourite shirts of the men   _____

2 The house of Stefan   _____

3 The food of the geese   _____

4 The boots of the gardeners   _____

5 The school of the children   _____

Add the apostrophes

Rewrite the sentences, adding the possessive apostrophes.

1   The cats tail curled around her bottom, like a snakes coils.

   _____

2   The dogs looked excited when they saw the cats whiskers.

   _____

3   The lions warm breath blew down the back of the mens necks.

   _____

4   The neighbours houses had a shared front garden.

   _____

Is the apostrophe right?

Put a tick or cross to show if these possessive apostrophes are in the right place.

1   Kate's rabbit   ☐   4   The cats' whiskers   ☐

2   Hassans' jumper   ☐   5   The mice's cheese   ☐

3   The mens' cars   ☐

Is it *its* or *it's*?

Circle the correct word – *its* or *it's*.

1   Its / It's   a beautiful day!

2   Its / It's   not fair!

3   What is   its / it's   name?

4   The horse has escaped again.
    Go and shut   its / it's   gate!

Top Tip *Make sure you learn where to use its and it's – people often get this wrong!*

It's not fair – Mel won't lend me her books!

That's because I'm as possessive over them as you are over your computer games!

Punctuation

Using punctuation

Put full stops and capital letters in this passage so it makes sense.

the woman looked surprised surely she had not heard the cat speak! she ought to rest more it must be overwork that was making her hear things if she was not careful, people would start thinking she was bonkers of course, she would never tell anyone what she thought she had heard cats meow, of course, but they do not usually strike up conversations with people!

Exclamation marks and question marks

Which is it? Should it be a question mark or exclamation mark? You decide!

1 What is the time

2 "Who's eaten my ice cream " bellowed Dad, angrily.

3 Can I come too

4 "Dreadful boy " shouted the angry girl.

5 What do you mean

Top Tip

If you are writing something and you are not sure if a sentence should end in a question mark, read it out loud. If it sounds like a question, add a question mark!

Commas

Commas are used to divide different parts of a sentence and help to make the meaning clear. Rewrite these sentences using commas so they make sense.

1 When the party was over the people went home.

_____

2 I like toffee chocolate vanilla and strawberry ice-cream.

_____

3 "What a pretty name" Shireen told Frances.

_____

4 The crocodile shot out of the water snapping as it went.

_____

Commas in lists

Put the commas in the right places in these lists.

1   The dog was a huge dirty shaggy mess.

2   I'd like a bar of chocolate some sherbet a lolly and an ice-cream please.

3   I've had two colds flu a fever and measles this winter!

4   The spider was huge hairy black and totally terrifying!

Semicolons

Semicolons can be used to break up lists, or to divide clauses in a sentence. A semicolon can make two sentences into one. Write these sentences using semicolons.

1   I shut my eyes. Soon it would be morning.

_____

2   I would love to go on holiday somewhere hot. Bermuda would be my choice.

_____

3   The animals all came into the ark. They were desperate to shelter from the rain.

_____

Colons

Colons can be used to introduce an explanation, or to show that a list is about to begin. Add the colons to the following sentences.

1   You will need cardboard, sticky tape and paper clips.

2   When you get to the shops, I would like eggs, milk, flour, potatoes and some shoelaces.

3   The party was over everyone had gone home.

4   Ingredients chocolate, crispy cereal and treacle.

Writing about speech

Reported speech

Reported speech means someone is telling the reader about something somebody else has said. Rewrite these sentences as reported speech. For example: *"I like apples," said Mrs Harris* becomes *Mrs Harris said she liked apples.*

1 "I love dogs!" said Trevor.

_____

2 "Cats are the most intelligent creatures in the universe," said Professor Newton.

_____

3 Dave said, "I'm going on holiday next week – and I can't wait!"

_____

4 Sheila yelled, "Get off my cabbages, you silly pigeons!"

_____

5 "Well, I'd love to, thanks very much," Tina laughed.

_____

Direct speech

Direct speech is the actual words that people say. Rewrite this reported speech as direct speech.

1 The boy said he wanted to go home.

_____

2 The man told me that he liked mushroom pizza best.

_____

3 They told me that they hated school.

_____

4 Cory said that he had not enjoyed the museum.

_____

5 The old man asked the girl what the time was.

_____

Punctuation

Speech marks always end with a punctuation mark inside the speech marks.

If someone is surprised or shouting, use an exclamation mark. If it is a question, use a question mark. Add the correct punctuation to these sentences.

1 "I think that's a great idea ____ " said Mr Nelson.

2 "Why can't I go, Mum ____ " asked Beth.

3 "It's time for bed, Alice – now ____ " called Dad.

4 "Is it dinnertime yet ____ " asked Rajan.

Not just said, but…

Circle the words in the box that could be used instead of 'said'.

yelled   slid   jumped   screamed   walked   sniggered   leaped   whispered
hooted   swam   asked   groaned   waltzed   giggled   squealed   sighed

Reported or direct?

Work out and note if these sentences are reported speech (R) or direct speech (D).

1 "Can I go out now, Mum?" ☐

2 She asked if she could go to the youth club. ☐

3 "So what?" yelled the boy. ☐

4 My mother told me I should always eat the right foods. ☐

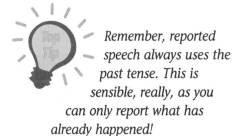

Remember, reported speech always uses the past tense. This is sensible, really, as you can only report what has already happened!

If people tell tales, is that reported speech?

I wouldn't know – I never tell tales, unlike SOME people I could mention…

Plurals

More than one

When you are writing or talking about more than one thing, it is called a plural. Usually, you just write a word and add an -s to the end to make it a plural. For example: *cat* becomes *cats*.

Add -s to make these words plural.

1 bird _____

2 flower _____

3 chair _____

4 boy _____

5 apple _____

6 snowflake _____

Tricky words

If a word already ends in -s, you cannot simply add another -s! Instead, you add -es. This is the same for words ending in -x. For example: *box* becomes *boxes*.

Add -es to these words to make them plural.

1 fox _____   **3** press _____

2 mess _____   **4** dress _____

Words ending in -y

Words that end in -y have special rules. Most words that end in -y lose the -y and add -ies. For example: *lady* becomes *ladies*.

Now try these.

1 pony _____   **4** fly _____

2 baby _____   **5** party _____

3 puppy _____   **6** country _____

Words ending in -f

When words end in -f and change from single to plural, there is a special rule: the -f changes to -ves. For example: *leaf* becomes *leaves*.

Now try these.

1 hoof   _____

2 calf   _____

3 dwarf _____

4 loaf   _____

Words ending in -o

When words ending in -o are changed from single to plural, there is a special rule: the -o stays and -es is added. For example: *echo* becomes *echoes*.

Now try these.

1 tomato _____

2 tornado _____

3 potato _____

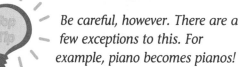

Be careful, however. There are a few exceptions to this. For example, piano becomes pianos!

The really odd ones!

Some plurals you just have to learn. It should not be hard, because they are quite odd!

Find the plurals of:

1 louse   _____

2 child   _____

3 formula _____

4 moose _____

5 goose   _____

6 man   _____

Ooh, scary thought – plural Mel!

Twice as nice!

Nouns and pronouns

What is a noun?

Nouns are naming words. The names of people, places, animals and things are all nouns. Underline the nouns.

1 The cat ran.   **2** The cake was sweet.   **3** The sky was dark.

4 The caterpillar changed.   **5** The sun shone.   **6** The dog barked.

Find the missing words

Fill in the missing words from the box below:

| place | nouns | repeating | same | pronouns |

What is a pronoun?

1 _____ do the same job as **2** _____. Words like he, she, it, mine and yours are all pronouns. They are used in the

3 _____ of nouns. They are very useful, because they stop you from **4** _____ yourself. If your writing was full of the

5 _____ words being repeated, it could easily become dull!

Using pronouns

Read the sentences below. Circle the correct nouns or pronouns to make the writing flow more easily.

1 Warren / He ate some cake, because Warren / he / him liked chocolate cake most of all. Warren / He ate it every chance that Warren / he / him got.

2 Mitzi / She went swimming, because that was Mitzi's / she / her favourite sport. Mitzi / She tried to go swimming every day, because Mitzi / she / her thought it would keep Mitzi / she / her healthy.

3 Harvey / He goes to school and Harvey / he / him likes school very much. Harvey / He likes doing science best of all, because Harvey / he / him likes learning about animals.

Letts KS2 Success

Workbook Answer Booklet

English

ANSWERS

Reading

PAGES 4–5 RESEARCH

Research for an article

research carried out properly and presented in the form of an article

Research for a leaflet

research carried out properly and presented in the form of a leaflet

Research for a web page

research carried out properly and presented in the form of a web page

Research for a report

research carried out properly and presented in the form of a report

PAGES 6–7 THE LANGUAGE OF BOOKS

The words used with books

1 a long number on the back of a book used to catalogue or order it
2 to find or order a book
3 at the back
4 information on the back of a book to make you want to read it
5 writes books
6 draws pictures to illustrate books

More terms

1 An appendix is used to give the reader more information about a particular subject raised in a book; it is a collection of extra material, found at the end of a book.
2 to give the meanings of words, a little like a dictionary
3 writing that is not 'made up'
4 'made up' writing, not real-life stories
5 an alphabetical list of contents in a book that helps the reader to find particular subjects
6 extra bits of information or explanations found at the bottom of a page

Parenthesis 1

1 brackets
2 writing
3 information
4 parenthesis
5 interruptions/afterthoughts
6 afterthoughts/interruptions

Parenthesis 2

1 E   2 E   3 A   4 E   5 A

PAGES 8–9 DESCRIPTION AND IMAGERY

Write your own similes

For example:

1 like foaming bath water
2 like a glowing orange, thrown into the sky
3 like a tiger stalking her prey
4 like a coiling snake
5 like a troll waiting under a bridge
6 like a mouse in a hang-glider

Write your own metaphors

For example:

1 is a flower petal
2 is a ruby
3 is a cherry
4 is a tiny iceberg
5 is an emerald carpet
6 is liquid honey

Personification

1 Autumn → is a woman with copper hair and a dress made from leaves.
2 Snow → is a beautiful lady dressed in diamonds and white fur.
3 Spring → is a chubby little boy, dressed in green. His moods change from the temper of the blustering wind to the warmth of a sunny smile in minutes!

PAGES 10–11 ALLITERATION AND ONOMAOTAPOEIA

Find the alliteration

1 <u>Slimy slugs slide</u> across the path.
2 <u>Pink pigs prefer</u> to eat <u>potatoes</u>.
3 <u>Dreadful, dangerous dragons</u> breathe flames.
4 <u>Ghastly, gruesome ghouls groan</u> in haunted castles.
5 <u>Cheeky chipmunks chirrup</u> at the birds as they steal their nuts.

Think up words

words that alliterate with 'sun' in the sun shape; words that alliterate with 'moon' in the moon shape

Match the words

1 slimy → slugs
2 sizzling → sausages
3 furry → foxes
4 sparkling → sea
5 giggling → girls

2

Find the onomatopoeia
Circled words are:
pop, smash, slurp, wobble and crash.

PAGES 12–13 SPECIAL WORDS
Idioms
1 weather
2 finger
3 hot
4 biscuit

Explain the idiom
1 not feeling very well
2 outrageous; the last word in cheek
3 sometimes friendly, sometimes not – very changeable
4 Calm down!

Matching proverbs
1 A stitch in time → saves nine.
2 Too many cooks → spoil the broth.
3 A bird in the hand → is worth two in the bush.

What proverbs mean
1 Putting things right straight away saves time and effort later.
2 Involving too many people can make things difficult to do.
3 A sure thing is better than many things that you may achieve.

Clichés
1 It's raining → cats and dogs
2 At the end of → the day
3 Starting on a → level playing field
4 As sick as → a parrot

PAGES 14–15 AMBIGUITY
Spot the real meaning!
1 The dog was bored.
2 Throw the dinner away if the dog doesn't want to eat it.
3 The girl was being nasty, so her mother scolded her.

Making sense
1 unclear/ambiguous
2 ambiguous/unclear
3 sentences
4 pronouns
5 clear

Make it clear!
Many answers are possible, for instance:
1 The fox was hungry, so he/she ate the rabbit.
2 The man was fierce, so he frowned at the boy.
3 The dog was lost, so the woman picked him up.

Using the words
1 When a sentence is ambiguous, the meaning is unclear and could mean more than one thing.
2 Ambiguous statements can lead to confusion.
3 a pronoun

More on making it clear!
Many answers are possible, for instance:
1 The butterfly was beautiful, so the monkey chased it.
2 Shushi decided that the dog's collar was too big, so she sold the collar.
3 The leak was repaired by the man before much damage could be done.
4 The huge shark ate the fish.

PAGES 16–17 READING INVESTIGATION
a completed bookbug!

Writing

PAGES 18–19 CONTRACTIONS
Missing words
1 letters
2 apostrophe
3 missed
4 informal
5 friends
6 speaking
7 formal

Contractions in full
1 will not
2 cannot
3 you have
4 they are
5 do not
6 she will

Matching contractions
1 I cannot → I can't
2 I am → I'm
3 I have → I've
4 we are → we're

5 do not → don't
6 I had → I'd
7 I would → I'd

Shorten the words
1 The boys **wouldn't** go to bed.
2 I **won't** be able to come to the party.
3 **We're** going out now.
4 **You've** got to be quiet!
5 **I'm** going to the shops now.

Take away the contractions
1 I **cannot** do it!
2 I **would not** like to go anywhere cold.
3 No **it is** not!
4 It **does not** matter.
5 **I have** a huge bowl of sweets.

PAGES 20–21 APOSTROPHES
Apostrophe + s
1 The baby's ball.
2 The man's hat.
3 The girl's coat.
4 The teacher's sweets.
5 The dog's collar.

Words that already end with s
1 The cats' paws were pink.
2 The ladies' hats were all huge.
3 The girls' bikes were new.
4 The boys' trousers were all blue.

More possessive apostrophes
1 the men's shirts
2 Stefan's house
3 the geese's food
4 the gardeners' boots
5 the children's school

Add the apostrophes
1 cat's tail/snake's coils
2 cat's whiskers (or cats' whiskers)
3 lion's warm breath/men's necks
4 neighbours' houses

Is the apostrophe right?
1 ✔ 2 ✘ 3 ✘ 4 ✔ 5 ✔

Is it *its* or *it's*?
1 It's 2 It's 3 its 4 its

PAGES 22–23 PUNCTUATION
Using punctuation
The woman looked surprised. **S**urely she had not heard the cat speak! **S**he ought to rest more. **I**t must be overwork that was making her hear things. **I**f she was not careful, people would start thinking she was bonkers. **O**f course, she would never tell anyone what she thought she had heard. **C**ats meow, of course, but they do not usually strike up conversations with people!

Exclamation marks and question marks
1 ? 2 ? 3 ? 4 ! 5 ?

Commas
1 When the party was over, the people went home.
2 I like toffee, chocolate, vanilla and strawberry ice-cream.
3 "What a pretty name," Shireen told Frances.
4 The crocodile shot out of the water, snapping as it went.

Commas in lists
1 The dog was a huge, dirty, shaggy mess.
2 I'd like a bar of chocolate, some sherbet, a lolly and an ice-cream please.
3 I've had two colds, flu, a fever and measles this winter!
4 The spider was huge, hairy, black and totally terrifying!

Semicolons
1 I shut my eyes; soon it would be morning.
2 I would love to go on holiday somewhere hot; Bermuda would be my choice.
3 The animals all came into the ark; they were desperate to shelter from the rain.

Colons
1 You will need: cardboard, sticky tape and paper clips.
2 When you get to the shops, I would like: eggs, milk, flour, potatoes and some shoelaces.
3 The party was over: everyone had gone home.
4 Ingredients: chocolate, crispy cereal and treacle.

PAGES 24–25 WRITING ABOUT SPEECH
Reported speech
1 Trevor said that he loved dogs.
2 Professor Newton said that cats were the most intelligent creatures in the universe.
3 Dave said that he was going on holiday next week and he couldn't wait.
4 Sheila yelled at the pigeons that they were silly and they should get off her cabbages.
5 Tina laughed and said she would love to and then said thanks very much.

Direct speech

1 "I want to go home," said the boy.
2 "I like mushroom pizza best," the man told me.
3 "We hate school," they told me.
4 "I didn't enjoy the museum," said Cory.
5 "What time is it?" the old man asked the girl.

Punctuation

1 "I think that's a great idea!" said Mr Nelson.
2 "Why can't I go, Mum?" asked Beth.
3 "It's time for bed, Alice – now!" called Dad.
4 "Is it dinnertime yet?" asked Rajan.

Not just said, but…

Circled words are:

yelled, screamed, sniggered, whispered, hooted, asked, groaned, giggled, squealed and sighed.

Reported or direct?

1 D   2 R   3 D   4 R

PAGES 26–27 PLURALS

More than one

1 birds
2 flowers
3 chairs
4 boys
5 apples
6 snowflakes

Tricky words

1 foxes
2 messes
3 presses
4 dresses

Words ending in -y

1 ponies
2 babies
3 puppies
4 flies
5 parties
6 countries

Words ending in -f

1 hooves
2 calves
3 dwarves
4 loaves

Words ending in -o

1 tomatoes
2 tornadoes
3 potatoes

The really odd ones!

1 lice
2 children
3 formulae
4 moose
5 geese
6 men

PAGES 28–29 NOUNS AND PRONOUNS

What is a missing words

1 The cat ran.
2 The cake was sweet.
3 The sky was dark.
4 The caterpillar changed.
5 The sun shone.
6 The dog barked.

Find the missing words

1 pronouns
2 nouns
3 place
4 repeating
5 same

Using pronouns

1 Warren ate some cake, because he liked chocolate cake most of all. He ate it every chance that he got.
2 Mitzi went swimming, because that was her favourite sport. She tried to go swimming every day, because she thought it would keep her healthy.
3 Harvey goes to school and he likes school very much. He likes doing science best of all, because he likes learning about animals.

Be careful!

1 They
2 them
3 they
4 they
5 them
6 they

Make a pronouns collection

check the child's pronouns

Nouns and pronouns

1 The **cat (N)** meowed, because **she (P)** was hungry.
2 The **girl (N)** laughed, because **she (P)** was happy.
3 The **snake (N)** slithered away, because **it (P)** was scared.
4 The **spider (N)** scuttled off, because **it (P)** saw a hungry **bird (N)**.
5 **Susan (N)** and **Karim (N)** saw the **bus (N)**, so **they (P)** started to run.

PAGES 30–31 ADJECTIVES

What are adjectives?
1 The <u>tabby</u> cat
2 The <u>slippery</u> slug
3 The <u>enormous</u> doorway
4 The <u>magenta</u> ribbon
5 The <u>glittering</u> sea
6 The <u>loud</u>, <u>angry</u> man

Making your writing exciting
For example:
1 The fat, hairy spider hid in the darkness.
2 The huge, red balloon floated away into the sky.
3 The fragrant, pink flower grew in the garden.

Exciting options!
For example:
1 violet, lilac
2 crimson, scarlet
3 azure, sapphire
4 golden, honey
5 chocolate, coffee
6 navy, royal blue

It's not nice!
For example:
1 My grandad is really kind to me.
2 This ice-cream is delicious.
3 The weather is lovely today.
4 My cat's fur feels wonderful.
5 I thought the film was excellent.

Interesting alternatives
For example:
1 hilarious
2 tragic
3 vast
4 microscopic
5 intelligent
6 delicious

Dazzling descriptions!
For example:
1 speedy
2 sparkling
3 silken
4 vast
5 glittering
6 rubbery
7 molten
8 sporty
9 hideous
10 slippery

PAGES 32–33 VERBS AND ADVERBS

What are verbs?
1 The man <u>shouted</u>.
2 The girl <u>giggled</u>.
3 The shark <u>chewed</u>.
4 The bell <u>rang</u>.
5 The firework <u>fizzed</u>.

Passive verbs
1 The cat was (stroked.)
2 The paper was (folded.)
3 The dog was (walked.)
4 The girl was (taken) to school.
5 The baby was (cuddled.)
6 The dinner was (cooked.)

Active verbs
1 I (stroked) the cat.
2 Dad (folded) the paper.
3 Alexander (walked) the dog.
4 Beth (took) the girl to school.
5 Ellie (cuddled) the baby.
6 Lily (cooked) the dinner.

Tenses
Many answers are possible, for instance:
1 I shall walk on the beach.
2 He will read a horror story.
3 I shall go Christmas shopping.
4 Susie will write to her friend.
5 The cat will sleep in front of the fire.

What are adverbs?
1 The lion roared <u>fiercely</u>.
2 The sun shone <u>brightly</u>.
3 The stream flowed <u>quickly</u>.
4 The snow fell <u>thickly</u>.
5 The woman smiled <u>warmly</u>.
6 The storm raged <u>angrily</u>.

More about adverbs
1 The boy was (quite) scruffy.
2 The cake was (completely) ruined.
3 The dress was (very) beautiful.
4 The sky was (totally) dark.
5 The baby was (completely) hysterical.
6 The snail was (extremely) slow.

PAGES 34–35 BUILDING VOCABULARY

Build your own thesaurus!
For example:

big: huge massive enormous gargantuan vast

small: tiny minuscule microscopic diminutive

walked: wandered ambled meandered

smelly: whiffy stinky pongy
happy: delighted joyful ecstatic

PAGES 36–37 WRITING ABOUT A PERSON

Biography
a short biography of an admired person

Autobiography
a short autobiography

CV
a CV with relevant facts

PAGES 38–39 WRITING INSTRUCTIONS

Instructions
step-by-step instructions, correctly ordered, for making a card. Language used should be suitable for a younger child.

Recipes
step-by-step instructions, correctly ordered, for making lollies

PAGES 40–41 PERSUASIVE WRITING

Design a leaflet
completed leaflet, attractively set out on the subject of keeping a pet

Design a poster
attractive poster about band/TV show using persuasive language

PAGES 42–43 WRITING REPORTS

Writing reports for science
a report clearly describing the habitat chosen and the animals and plants that live there

Writing reports for geography
a geography report about the local area with lots of information about facilities available

PAGES 44–45 WRITING RECOUNTS

Recounting a game
a recount of a game played, including any funny anecdotes and the way the game ended

Recounting a film
a recount of the story of a film that has been watched and enjoyed – perhaps including the reasons why it was enjoyed

PAGES 46–47 WRITING STORIES
story written using the planning stages provided

PAGES 48–49 WRITING INVESTIGATION

Haiku
a haiku using the 5, 7, 5 pattern successfully

Kennings
an interesting, descriptive kenning for others to guess

Test practice

PAGES 50–56 TEST PRACTICE

Reading task
1   Thane of Glamis
2   three witches
3   King
4   his sons will be kings
5   because she and Macbeth could kill him there
6   hags, crones
7   Macbeth meets the witches with Banquo as they return from battle.
    King Duncan is murdered.
    Macduff's family is killed.
    Lady Macbeth goes mad.
    Macbeth's head is taken to Malcolm.
8   Macduff's soldiers disguise themselves with twigs and branches from Great Birnam Wood, making it look as if the wood is moving towards Dunsinane castle.
9   guilt from killing King Duncan; she washes invisible blood from her hands, then kills herself
10 many answers are possible

Writing task
1   a suitable plan, such as a flow chart or similar, and a recount of a day out
2   a suitable story plan and character ideas, plus a story with a strong beginning, good development and a strong ending

Published by Letts Educational an imprint of HarperCollins *Publishers*
77-85 Fulham Palace Road,London W6 8JB

Phone orders: 0844 576 8126
Fax orders: 0844 576 8131
Email: education@harpercollins.co.uk
Website: www.lettsandlonsdale.com

First published 2007
04/120609

Editorial and design: 2ibooks [publishing solutions] Cambridge

Colour Reprographics by PDQ

Author: Lynn Huggins-Cooper
Book concept and development: Helen Jacobs, Publishing Director
Project editor: Lily Morgan
Illustrators: Piers Baker and Pumpkin House
Cover design: Angela English

British Library Cataloging in Publication Data. A CIP record of this book is available from the British Library.

9781843157496

MIX
Paper from
responsible sources

FSC
www.fsc.org   FSC™ C007454

Be careful!

They and *them* are easy to mix up and so are *me* and *my*, so be careful. Circle the correct word in each sentence.

1 Them / They are lovely!

2 Do you like them / they?

3 Why are them / they going home?

4 What are them / they going to do?

5 What is wrong with them / they?

6 When are them / they arriving?

Make a pronouns collection

Pronouns are really useful words. You will already be using these words without realising that they are pronouns. The only new thing you need to learn is that they are called pronouns. For example: he, she, it, mine, yours, I, you, we, they, me, him, her, them and us.

To learn which words are pronouns, learn them like spellings.

Top Tip

Remember to read your work back to yourself. This will make sure you have not kept repeating nouns when a pronoun would make the work flow more naturally.

Nouns and pronouns

Mark the nouns (N) and the pronouns (P) in each sentence.

1 The cat ____ meowed, because she ____ was hungry.

2 The girl ____ laughed, because she ____ was happy.

3 The snake ____ slithered away, because it ____ was scared.

4 The spider ____ scuttled off, because it ____ saw a hungry bird ____.

5 Susan ____ and Karim ____ saw the bus ____, so they ____ started to run.

Sam's a noun!

And known by my friends and me as it – a pronoun!

Adjectives

What are adjectives?

Adjectives are describing words. (They describe a noun in a sentence.)
Underline the adjectives.

1 The tabby cat   2 The slippery slug   3 The enormous doorway

4 The magenta ribbon   5 The glittering sea   6 The loud, angry man

Making your writing exciting

Adjectives are a powerful tool for a writer. They are describing words, and exciting descriptions are what make people want to read more. Adjectives help to make vivid word pictures in the mind of your readers.

Top Tip — *Try to use unusual adjectives. Collect them in a notebook when you are reading.*

Compare these sentences:

The bear growled at the girls.

The ferocious black bear growled at the cowering girls.

Which sentence makes the best word picture? The sentence with adjectives, of course! Rewrite these sentences using adjectives to make them more interesting.

1 The spider hid in the darkness. _____

_____

2 The balloon floated away into the sky. _____

_____

3 The flower grew in the garden. _____

_____

Exciting options!

Why say pink when you can say magenta? Think of a more exciting adjective to replace each colour word.

1 The flower is purple _____   4 The sun is yellow _____

2 The apple is red   _____   5 The mud is brown _____

3 The sea is blue   _____   6 The jacket is blue _____

It's not nice!

Nice is a rather dull, overused adjective. Think of a more interesting adjective to replace nice in each sentence.

1   My grandad is really nice to me.   _____

2   This ice-cream is nice.   _____

3   The weather is nice today.   _____

4   My cat's fur feels nice.   _____

5   I thought the film was nice.   _____

Interesting alternatives

Choose a more interesting alternative for each adjective.

1   funny   _____   4   small   _____

2   sad   _____   5   clever   _____

3   big   _____   6   tasty   _____

Dazzling descriptions

Choose a suitable adjective to describe each of these nouns.

1   horse   _____   6   balloons   _____

2   snow   _____   7   chocolate   _____

3   butterfly   _____   8   car   _____

4   elephant   _____   9   alien   _____

5   stars   _____   10 snail   _____

You're not very nice sometimes, Mel!

No, you mean I'm vile – that's much more descriptive!

Verbs and adverbs

What are verbs?

Verbs are words that describe actions. Every sentence has to have a verb or it is not a sentence. Verbs tell you what a person or thing is doing. For example, in the sentence: *The fish is swimming*, the word *swimming* is the verb.

Underline the verbs.

1   The man shouted.

2   The girl giggled.

3   The shark chewed.

4   The bell rang.

5   The firework fizzed.

Passive verbs

Passive verbs tell you about what is being done. A sentence with a passive verb tells you about the thing or person that the action is happening to. It does not always say what or who is doing the action, though. For example, in the sentence: *'The window was polished'*, we do not know who did the polishing.

Circle the verbs.

1   The cat was stroked.   4   The girl was taken to school.

2   The paper was folded.   5   The baby was cuddled.

3   The dog was walked.   6   The dinner was cooked.

Active verbs

Active verbs tell you what is being done and who is doing it. For example, in the sentence, *'Marie polished the window'*, we know who polished the window – Marie.

Circle the verbs.

1   I stroked the cat.   4   Beth took the girl to school.

2   Dad folded the paper.   5   Ellie cuddled the baby.

3   Alexander walked the dog.   6   Lily cooked the dinner.

Tenses

Verbs change tense to show us when things happen – whether it is past, present (now) or future. For example:

- I ate the pizza. *Past*
- I am eating the pizza. *Present (now)*
- I shall eat the pizza. *Future*

Rewrite the verbs in the future tense.

1   I walked on the beach.   _____

2   He is reading a horror story.   _____

3   I went Christmas shopping.   _____

4   Susie is writing to her friend.   _____

5   The cat is sleeping in front of the fire.   _____

What are adverbs?

Adverbs are words that describe verbs. For example, in the sentence: *The shark swam quickly*, the word *quickly* is the adverb. It describes the verb *swam*, telling us how it was done.

Underline the adverbs.

1   The lion roared fiercely.   4   The snow fell thickly.

2   The sun shone brightly.   5   The woman smiled warmly.

3   The stream flowed quickly.   6   The storm raged angrily.

More about adverbs

Adverbs can also describe adjectives. Words like *completely*, *totally*, *quite* and *very* are used with adjectives to show how much the adjective is working on the noun. For example, in the sentence: *The woman was very cross*, the word *very* describes how cross she was.

Circle the adverbs that describe these adjectives.

1   The boy was quite scruffy.   4   The sky was totally dark.

2   The cake was completely ruined.   5   The baby was completely hysterical.

3   The dress was very beautiful.   6   The snail was extremely slow.

Building vocabulary

Build your own thesaurus!

A thesaurus is a book that gives the reader lots of different ways to say the same word. It helps writers to avoid their work becoming repetitive and boring.

For example, instead of said, you could use: *sighed, chuckled, laughed, bellowed, shouted* or *hooted*. Make a collection of interesting ways of saying:

Top Tip

Look in books and magazines as you are reading and make a collection of useful words in a notebook. You could arrange it in sections according to subject, for example space, animals or sea creatures.

Big

Not just big but...

_____

_____

_____

_____

_____

_____

Small

Not just small but...

_____

_____

_____

_____

_____

_____

_____

Walked

Not just walked but...

_____

_____

_____

_____

_____

Smelly

Not just smelly but...

_____

_____

_____

_____

_____

Happy

Not just happy but...

_____

_____

_____

_____

_____

Of course, my vocabulary is gargantuan...

No, that's just your mouth!

Writing about a person

Biography

Write a short biography of a person you admire – in the news or in history.

_____
_____
_____
_____
_____
_____
_____
_____
_____
_____
_____
_____

Autobiography

Write a short autobiography of your life so far!

_____
_____
_____
_____
_____
_____
_____
_____
_____
_____
_____
_____
_____

CV

Write your CV, as though you were applying for a job.

When you are writing a biography or autobiography, start with a timeline and work from there, adding details to each point on the timeline to build paragraphs.

My autobiography will be a very long book, because of all the brave deeds I've done...

It'll be very long, because it'll be so full of rubbish!

Writing instructions

Instructions

Imagine you are teaching a younger brother or sister how to make a birthday card for a relative. It could include pop-up pieces or a 'lift-the-flap'. Write a set of instructions to tell him/her what to do. Remember, provide a list of 'things you will need' as well as step-by-step instructions. If you are stumped for ideas, look in books or on the Internet.

_____

_____

_____

_____

_____

_____

_____

_____

_____

_____

_____

_____

_____

_____

_____

_____

_____

_____

_____

_____

_____

_____

Remember that your instructions MUST be in the correct order.

Recipes

Write a recipe for making fruit ice lollies with juice and chunks of fruit.

_____

_____

_____

_____

_____

_____

_____

_____

_____

_____

_____

_____

_____

_____

_____

_____

_____

_____

_____

_____

Let's make a card for grandad!

Aw...can't we just make lollies instead?!

Persuasive writing

Design a leaflet

Put together a leaflet about keeping an animal as a pet. It could be an animal you already have or one you would like, such as a tarantula. Carry out research to find out more, and then create a leaflet to encourage people to keep the animal as a pet.

Design a poster

Design a poster about your favourite band or TV show. Use persuasive language to provoke interest. Make your poster using a computer programme, and drag and drop photos or clip art onto the poster. Then print it out and hang it on the wall!

Top Tip *Bright colours and text boxes will help your writing to stand out so that people take notice.*

I'm going to write a note to pursuade Mum to give me more pocket money!

Fat chance!

Writing reports

Writing reports for science

You often need to write reports in science. Choose a local habitat that you find interesting, such as the seashore, the garden or a pond, and write a report about it. Give details of the animals and plants that live there, and write something about their interesting habits. Look in books and on the Internet to find out more.

_____
_____
_____
_____
_____
_____
_____
_____
_____
_____
_____
_____
_____
_____
_____
_____
_____
_____
_____
_____
_____
_____
_____

Writing reports for geography

Write a report about your local area. Are there lots of facilities for the community? Interview friends and family and find out what they think. You may even like to create a survey and report your findings. If your area has a local paper or newsletter, you could submit your report to them!

_____

_____

_____

_____

_____

_____

_____

_____

_____

_____

_____

_____

_____

_____

_____

_____

_____

_____

_____

_____

_____

_____

_____

_____

_____

_____

_____

Top Tip _Look in newsletters, magazines and newspapers to see examples of reports to remind you of the type of language used._

Writing recounts

Recounting a game

Write a recount of the last game you played with your friends. It could be a game you played outside, a board game or a sport. Remember to say how the game ended!

_____

_____

_____

_____

_____

_____

_____

_____

_____

_____

_____

_____

_____

_____

_____

_____

_____

_____

_____

_____

_____

_____

_____

_____

_____

Recounting a film

Write a recount of a film you have enjoyed.

_____
_____
_____
_____
_____
_____
_____
_____
_____
_____
_____
_____
_____
_____
_____
_____
_____
_____
_____
_____
_____

Top Tip *Don't forget to use words that tell the reader about the order in which things happened, such as 'next...then...finally'.*

I'm going to design a poster for *Cold Treason*. They're a great rock band!

I'll take some persuading...I prefer pop!

Writing stories

Write a story using one of these story starters

a The noise filtered into my dream. It was a wailing, like something in pain...or something very scared. I woke with a start.

b Jackie could not believe her luck. A whole month abroad! Nobody else she knew had ever been away for that long. This holiday was going to be amazing.

c She watched the rain as it ran in channels down the cracked window. What a dump!

The best way to improve your story writing is to read more stories...so get down to the library!

Cluster of ideas and exciting vocabulary

Character profile

_____

_____

_____

_____

_____

_____

_____

_____

Problem for the characters to solve

_____
_____
_____
_____
_____
_____
_____
_____

Good strong ending

_____
_____
_____
_____
_____
_____
_____
_____

Now write your story!

Writing investigation

Be a poet!

Poetry is a great source of descriptive and wonderful words. Look at the examples below.

Try to read a variety of poems. Look for poetry collections in the library at school.

Top Tip

Haiku

Haiku are Japanese poems with a special pattern of 17 syllables: 5, 7, 5. Have you read any haiku during the literacy hour at school?

Read this haiku:

Beloved grey cat (5)

Curls up softly in my lap (7)

Funny, loyal friend. (5)

Now write your own haiku. You could write it about a pet or even about your favourite food.

Kennings

Kennings are a way of describing things without actually saying what they are. A poem can be made by making a list of kennings. Read this poem and try to guess what it is about!

Sticky-slitherer

Lettuce-eater

Mucus-bubbler

Glossy-egg-layer

Antennae-wiggler

Now write your own kennings poem. You could make a booklet with your poem on one side and the answer on the right-hand side under a flap, so people have to guess the answer!

I'd love to be a poet...

Well, you're certainly good at making things up!

Test practice

Reading task

Mystery, murder and suspense – it is all to be found in Shakespeare's Macbeth!

Read the following synopsis, then answer the questions over the page.

Three foul witches meet on a wild, windswept heath. They are casting evil spells and incantations, and discussing the next time they will meet – and they reveal that Macbeth will be there.

Macbeth was the Thane of Glamis. He was a brave warrior, fighting as a champion of the King. Returning from the battle with his friend Banquo, he sees the witches. Cackling and mixing hideous potions, they predict that he will become first Thane of Cawdor, then King. They also say that Banquo will be father to Kings himself. Macbeth has ambitions, but he knows that King Duncan and his sons, Malcolm and Donalbain, are alive and well. Suddenly, they meet messengers from King Duncan who declare Macbeth Thane of Cawdor! The witches' prediction is beginning to come true, and Macbeth bubbles with excitement.

When they arrive at court, King Duncan declares that he has made his son, Malcolm, heir to the throne. Macbeth smiles, but feels sharp disappointment. Duncan then says that the royal party will travel to Macbeth's castle and spend the night there.

Macbeth dashes off ahead and tells his wife, Lady Macbeth. She is a cruel and ambitious woman. Since Macbeth sent her a letter telling her of the witches' prediction, she has been planning evil. Now she feels fate has played into her hands and tells Macbeth that the King should die in the night. Macbeth is shocked and shrinks from her. Lady Macbeth is a clever and persuasive woman and she manages to get her husband to agree to her plan. They are going to murder Duncan and blame his servants!

Macbeth waits until everyone is in bed, and creeps towards the King's chamber clutching his daggers. Suddenly, he sees a bloodstained dagger suspended in the air in front of him, but try as he might, he cannot grasp it. He sweeps into the King's chamber and commits the murder, coming back out clutching the daggers. Lady Macbeth takes the daggers from him and takes them back into the chamber so that the servants will be blamed.

A loud knocking sounds through the castle and the doors are opened to reveal Macduff. He needs to see the King. When he enters the chamber and finds the King dead, he runs out shouting for help. Macbeth kills the servants and this makes Macduff suspicious. Donalbain and Malcolm leave the castle, fearing for their own lives, and Macbeth is made King.

Macbeth worries that Banquo's sons will be Kings, as foretold by the witches, and that Banquo himself may suspect him of Duncan's murder. He decides to hold a banquet and invites Banquo. Banquo and his son ride out to hunt and Macbeth sends assassins after them. When the men return, they report that they have murdered Banquo but his son, Fleance, has escaped.

That night, Macbeth looks for his seat at the feast, saying that the table is full. He is shown a place, but all he can see is Banquo, with his throat slit. No one else can see the dreadful shadow. Macbeth is so worried that Lady Macbeth sends everyone away.

Later that night, Macbeth goes to see the witches. He is told by the hags that he should beware of Macduff and that Banquo's descendants will rule as Kings for generations. The crones also tell him that he will not be beaten until 'Great Birnam Wood shall come to Dunsinane'.

Macbeth sends assassins to kill Macduff, but he has already fled. They kill his family and Macduff swears revenge. He assembles an army and attacks Macbeth. Lady Macbeth has gone mad, and she walks the castle washing invisible blood from her hands. In her madness, she kills herself.

A messenger comes to say that Birnam Wood is attacking – all Macduff's men are carrying branches as cover. Macduff enters the castle and fights with Macbeth. Macduff slaughters Macbeth, the murderer, and cuts off his head. He takes it to Malcolm, the new King.

Choose the best words from the boxes to complete each sentence.

1 At the very beginning of the story, Macbeth is _____

King of England   Thane of Cawdor   Thane of Glamis   very tired

2 Banquo and Macbeth meet _____

three crows   three toads   three ghosts   three witches

3 The witches tell Macbeth that in the future he will be _____

old   ill   King   Thane of Fife

4 Banquo is told that _____

his sons will be killed   his sons will be soldiers
his sons will be kings   his sons will be Thanes

5 Why was Lady Macbeth happy when she heard that King Duncan would sleep at her castle?

_____

_____

_____

6 Find two words in the story that have the same meaning as witches.

_____   _____

7 Put these events in order, numbering them from 1 to 5.

☐ King Duncan is murdered.

☐ Macbeth meets the witches with Banquo as they return from battle.

☐ Macduff's family is killed.

☐ Lady Macbeth goes mad.

☐ Macbeth's head is taken to Malcolm.

8 How did the hags' prediction about how the 'Great Birnam Wood shall come to Dunsinane' come true?

_____

_____

_____

_____

_____

_____

_____

9 Why do you think Lady Macbeth went mad? What did her madness make her do?

_____

_____

_____

_____

_____

_____

10 Did you enjoy the story? Give reasons to support your answers.

_____

_____

_____

_____

_____

_____

Writing task

1   Write a recount of an exciting day out that you have enjoyed with friends or family. Don't forget to start with a plan, such as a flow diagram or a timeline.

Plan your recount here.

Now write your recount here.

_____

_____

_____

_____

_____

_____

_____

_____

_____

_____

_____

_____

_____

2 You are now going to practise planning and writing stories. Apart from being fun, you may choose to write a story for your SATs test.

Follow all the stages of writing a story:

clustering ideas

story plan

character profile

story starter

strong ending

Remember to ask yourself:

Where does your story begin?

Does the story setting help to build atmosphere? (For example, if it is a ghost story, is the story set in a spooky place?)

Who is going to appear in your story? Do you have a main character? Are there any heroes or villains?

Have you thought of a gripping beginning to hook your reader so that they want to read more?

How does the story develop? Are there any major changes or surprises during the story?

Have you done a character profile?

Have you thought of a good strong ending? Is there a twist in the tale (something unexpected at the end)?

Now plan your story here.

Now write your story here. Use spare paper if you need to.

_____

_____

_____

_____

_____

_____

_____

_____

_____

_____

_____

_____

_____

_____

_____

_____

_____

_____

_____

_____

_____

_____

_____

_____

_____

_____

_____

_____

_____

     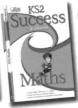 

ACKNOWLEDGEMENTS

Published by Letts Educational
an imprint of HarperCollins*Publishers*
77–85 Fulham Palace Road
London W6 8JB

First published 2007

7050811

Text © Lynn Huggins-Cooper
Design and illustration © 2006 Letts Educational

Every effort has been made to trace copyright holders and obtain their permission for the use of copyright material. The author and publisher will gladly receive information enabling them to rectify any error or omission in subsequent editions.

All facts are correct at time of going to press.

All rights reserved. No part of the publication may be produced, stored in a retrieval system, or transmitted, in any form or by any means, electronic, mechanical, photocopying, recording or otherwise without the prior permission of Letts Educational.

British Library Cataloging in Publication Data. A CIP record of this book is available from the British Library.

9781843157496

Editorial and design: 2ibooks [publishing solutions] Cambridge

Colour Reprographics by PDQ

Author: Lynn Huggins-Cooper
Book concept and development: Helen Jacobs
Project editor: Lily Morgan
Illustrator: Piers Baker and Pumpkin House
Cover design: Angela English

Printed in China

MIX
Paper from responsible sources
FSC® C007454

FSC™ is a non-profit international organisation established to promote the responsible management of the world's forests. Products carrying the FSC label are independently certified to assure consumers that they come from forests that are managed to meet the social, economic and ecological needs of present and future generations, and other controlled sources.

Find out more about HarperCollins and the environment at www.harpercollins.co.uk/green

5 EASY WAYS TO ORDER

1. Visit our website: www.lettsandlonsdale.com
2. Fax your order to 0844 576 8131
3. Phone us on 0844 576 8126
4. Email us at education@harpercollins.co.uk
5. Post your order to: Collins Education, Freepost GW2446, Glasgow G64 1BR

KS2 Success

Workbook

English

The simple way to Key Stage 2 Test Success...
...developed with teachers and students to create
the ideal revision series.

All the assessment practice your child needs, presented in a clear,
colourful layout designed to make revision simple and fun.

- **Step-by-step testing** – on all Revision Guide topics
- **Topic sections** – make revision focus easy
- **Investigations** – put learning in context
- **Top Tips** – give useful advice
- **Test-style questions** – offer assessment practice

With accompanying
Revision Guide, covering
all KS2 topics. See inside
back cover for details of
how to order.

Take a look inside and see for yourself!

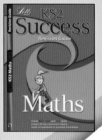
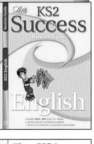

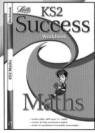
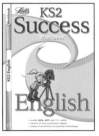

ISBN 978-1-84315-749-6

9 781843 157496

www.lettsandlonsdale.co

£3.99

Sets

A&B

KEY STAGE 2
Levels 3–5

Instructions,
Answers and
Mark Scheme
Booklet

English

Instructions and
Answers

Instructions, Answers and Mark Scheme Booklet

This booklet provides advice on how to administer the tests, as well as supplying the answers and the mark schemes for each of the test papers.

On page 30, there is a grid to record your child's marks in and a guide showing how these marks relate to levels.

Contents

Instructions on using the Practice Papers

Understanding the SATs

What are the SATs?
SATs are taken by pupils at the end of Year 2 in English and Mathematics. Teacher assessments will form the main part of the child's result. However, National Tests will validate the teacher's own assessment. There are no tests in Science until Year 6.

What are the children tested on?
The children are tested on all of the work they have covered in all year groups so far. Year 6 children are tested on Maths, English and Science. Years 3, 4 and 5 are only tested in Maths and English, and have Science assessments throughout the year.

What SATs will my child take?
The exact format of the tests depends on the year, but this is a typical breakdown:

> **English**
> **Reading** (45 minutes + 15 mins reading time)
> **Writing** Long 45 minutes and short 20 minutes
> **Spelling** 10 mins
> **Handwriting**

> **Maths**
> **Mental Maths** (20 minutes)
> **Written paper** (45 minutes)
> **Written paper** (45 minutes)

> **Science** Year 6 only
> **Science (paper A)** 45 minutes
> **Science (paper B)** 45 minutes

* No statutory testing is carried out at KS1.

What do the English tests assess in my child?
All children study the National Curriculum from Year 1. At the end of Year 2, the tests will assess your child's knowledge, skills and understanding in the programmes of study that they have followed from Year 1.

In the Reading Test your child is assessed against seven different Assessment Focus (AF) criteria. These take into account a range of aspects of your child's reading which are assessed in the SATs tests:

AF1   Use a range of strategies, including accurate decoding of text, to read for meaning.

AF2   Understand, describe, select or retrieve information, events or ideas from texts, and use quotation and reference to text.

AF3   Deduce, infer or interpret information, events or ideas from texts.

AF4   Identify and comment on the structure and organisation of texts, including grammatical and presentational features at text level.

AF5   Explain and comment on the writers' use of language, including grammatical and literary features at word and sentence level.

AF6   Identify and comment on the writers' purposes and viewpoints, and the overall effect of text on the reader.

AF7   Relate texts to their social, cultural and historical contexts and literary traditions.

(Source: QCA 2004 mark scheme)

Can my child fail a SATs test?

It is important that children understand they are not going to 'pass' or 'fail' the test – it will just show what they have learned and what they can do.

About these Practice Papers

1   These test papers are similar to the one your child will take at the end of Year 6. The papers provide a good idea of strengths and weaknesses of your child's subject knowledge.

2   The answers and mark scheme have been provided to allow you to check how your child has done.

3   When an area of weakness has been identified, it is useful to go over these and similar types of questions with your child. Sometimes your child will be familiar with the subject matter but might not understand what the question is asking. This will become apparent when talking to your child.

Tips for the top

1   Don't make silly mistakes. Make sure you emphasise to your child the importance of reading the question. Easy marks can be picked up by just doing as the question asks.

2   Make your answers clearly legible. If your child has made a mistake, encourage them to put a cross through it and write the correct answer clearly next to it. Try to encourage your child to use an eraser as little as possible.

3   Don't panic! These practice papers, and indeed the end of Key Stage 2 SATs, are meant to provide teachers with a guide to the level a child has aspired to. They are not the be all and end all. Explain to your child that there is no need to worry if they cannot do a question, just go on to the next question and come back to it later if they have time.

Taking the Tests

1   Make sure you provide your child with a quiet environment where they can complete their test undisturbed.

2   Provide your child with the following equipment: pencil, ruler and eraser (rubber).

3   The Test Papers vary in the amount of time given so always consult the front page of each paper. The Reading Tests are both 1 hour long, the Long Writing tests are both 45 minutes long and the Short Writing Tests are both 20 minutes. They should be given 15 minutes to read through the booklet and 45 minutes to answer the questions.

4   You may only read the instructions to your child.

Reading Test

Although each Assessment Focus is tested, you should note that AF1 is not done so separately.

By the end of Key Stage 2 it is expected that your child is using "a range of strategies, including accurate decoding of text, to read for meaning". The majority of questions in the Reading Test are concerned with AF3. In the 2003 paper, 54% of marks were given to AF3 and in 2004 the figure was 44%.

In the Mark Scheme for each Reading Test, the AF is identified for each question. On marking each paper, these will help you and your child to identify areas of strength and weakness in their comprehension skills. When your child is reading you will then be able to devise questions similar to those for each AF and develop comprehension skills in this way.

Before marking the Reading Test, ensure that you read the Reading Booklet for that test. This will help to clarify the mark scheme and will also help you to judge whether the content of an answer is correct. Different children have different ways of wording a correct answer – you need to judge whether your child "had the right idea".

Mark Scheme for Set A Reading Test Paper "On Track"

Section 1: "The Green Dragon and the Old Gentleman"

1 the Green Dragon   *AF2 (1 mark)*
2 his hand   *AF2 (1 mark)*
3 wave to the Green Dragon   *AF2 (1 mark)*
4 take their love to father   *AF2 (1 mark)*
5 could be treated like a pet   *AF3 (1 mark)*
6 Award 1 mark for each of the following points (up to a maximum of 2 marks).
   The trains made sounds like home/reminded them of the streets of London.   *AF3 (1 mark)*
   They thought it might be going to where their father was.   *AF3 (1 mark)*
7 Award 2 marks for answers which make a comparison between the
   power/ferocity/awe of the train and that of a dragon and that it was as if/easy to imagine
   that the tunnel was the lair in which the dragon lived. Award 1 mark for answers which   *AF5*
   relate to the train or tunnel being like a dragon or its lair.   *(1–2 marks)*
8 Award 3 marks for fuller explanations which refer to the children thinking that the
   train is going to where their father is, their idea of sending their love to their father
   by the train and that they thought perhaps the old gentleman knew their father.
   Award 2 marks for an explanation which includes two of the above points and   *AF3*
   award 1 mark for an explanation which includes just one of the above points.   *(1–3 marks)*
9 a) Award 1 mark for any reference to the use of handkerchiefs as a means of
      being more easily noticed.   *AF3 (1 mark)*
   b) Award 1 mark for reference to the fact that they were too excited or that they
      were children and the cleanliness of their handkerchiefs did not bother them.   *AF3 (1 mark)*
10 Award 1 mark for a brief explanation which suggests that Bobbie is looking after
   her siblings and reassures them.   *AF3 (1 mark)*

Section 2: "*The Railway Children* – From Book to Screen"

11 Award 1 mark for a brief explanation that it provides an overview of the fact that
   the section is about the book being made into a television programme/film.   *AF5 (1 mark)*
12 Award 1 mark for a brief explanation that the text shows that although it started
   life as a book it eventually found its way onto screen as a television programme
   and/or films.   *AF6 (1 mark)*
13 Award 1 mark (up to maximum of 2 marks) for inclusion of any of the following.
   Members of the Royal Family were guests at the premiere.
   At Christmas 1970 it was shown privately to the Queen and other members of
   the Royal Family.
   It was voted among the best one hundred British Pictures of the past century.   *AF2*
   It is included in the Chicago Museum of Fine Arts.   *(1–2 marks)*

Section 3: "An Interview With the Railway Children"

14 Award 2 marks for a fuller explanation of the feeling that modern-day children
   have to grow up a lot quicker compared to children in the past. Award 1 mark for
   a simple response stating that children today are treated as young adults from   *AF7*
   an earlier age (without comparison to the past).   *(1–2 marks)*
15 Award 1 mark for a reference to the fact that they were dressed in
   Edwardian costume.   *AF3 (1 mark)*
16 Award 1 mark for reference to the restricted movement, feeling like a doll or
   feeling younger.   *AF2 (1 mark)*

Section 4: "A Small World"

17 Award 3 marks for fuller explanations which refer to the increased speed and convenience of travel when the railways came along. There should also be reference to this speed and convenience making distant places more easily accessible, thus making it seem like the world is now smaller. Award 2 marks for reference to increased speed, convenience and accessibility but no reference to a shrinking world. Award 1 mark for a simple reference to any of speed, convenience or accessibility. *AF7 (3 marks)*

18 Award 2 marks for the correct order of: (1) Trevithick tests the first steam locomotive (given); (2) The Rocket wins the Rainhill Trials; (3) The Mallard sets the world record; (4) The Japanese Bullet train makes its first journey. Award 1 mark for one event in the correct place (in addition to that given). *AF2 (1–2 marks)*

19 Award 1 mark for reference to the use of new technology/diesel trains/ electric trains. *AF3 (1 mark)*

20 Award 2 marks for an explanation that the timeline provides a visual aid to support the text and that it enables other events/facts to be easily placed alongside information already given. Award 1 mark for a reference to either of the above points. *AF4 (1–2 marks)*

21 Award 1 mark for a brief explanation that these passages have been used to show the advance in trains from the early days to modern high speed trains. *AF4 (1 marks)*

Section 5: "Travelling in Style"

22 Award 2 marks for all the correct pairings of: fine views – through the windows (given); a piano – in the bar; wood panelling – in the compartments; finest crystal glasses – in the dining car. *AF2 (1–2 marks)*

23 2 marks for an explanation that the train is long and "snake-like", and that its journey will be a winding one. Award 1 mark for reference to either of the above points. *AF5 (1–2 marks)*

24 Award 2 marks for correctly identifying: wealthy, luxury, rich, romantic. Award 1 mark for correct identification of 2 or 3 of these words. *AF5 (1–2 marks)*

25 Award 1 mark for reference to a personal steward. *AF3 (1 mark)*

Section 6: The whole booklet

26 Award 2 marks for a response of "yes" or "no" with a full explanation of the reason. e.g. Yes because trains are big and fast and you can see different things from them. Trains are exciting because most of the time people go to places in cars. OR No, because we have cars and aeroplanes now and people don't need to use trains as much. Children have many more technologies to be excited about. Award 1 mark for explanations which cover only single points. *AF7 (1–2 marks)*

27 Award 2 marks for an explanation which refers to the inclusion of the article to show that rail travel is still seen as glamorous by some people and that there can be more to rail travel than simply getting from one place to another. Award 1 mark for an explanation which refers to just one of the above points. *AF6 (1–2 marks)*

28 Award 2 marks for reference to the fact that trains run on railway tracks and/or that the content of the booklet is about trains and (by default) railway tracks. Award 1 mark for a single point. *AF6 (1–2 marks)*

29 Award 2 marks for an explanation which refers to such a web-site existing so people can find further information about *The Railway Children* and to serve as a focal point for fans of the book, the film and trains. Award 1 mark for reference to one of the above points. *AF3 (1–2 marks)*

30 Award 3 marks for a fuller explanation which refers to the use of fiction and non-fiction elements to indicate the development of rail travel, the early fascination with trains and railways (particularly illustrated by the extract from the book) and modern-day interest (particularly illustrated by the "From Book to Screen" article and the "Travelling in Style" article). Reference should be made to sections of the text in the response. Award 2 marks for an explanation which does not cover all of the above points but does refer to some of the sections of text. Award 1 mark for an explanation which covers any of the above points without reference to *AF6* the sections of text. *(1–3 marks)*

The following table shows the breakdown of marks for each Assessment Focus in the Reading Test for Set A. Using the Mark Schemes, total the number of marks your child has scored against each Assessment Focus. This will provide you with a good idea of areas of strength and areas for development in their comprehension skills.

	Max Score	Score
AF2	11	
AF3	14	
AF4	3	
AF5	7	
AF6	8	
AF7	7	

Mark Scheme for Set B Reading Test Paper "Polar Explorer"

Section 1: "Polar Dream"

1	walking and skiing	*AF2 (1 mark)*
2	scare away polar bears	*AF2 (1 mark)*
3	went to live with Helen	*AF2 (1 mark)*
4	carry her supplies	*AF3 (1 mark)*
5	Polar Dream	*AF2 (1 mark)*

6 Award 1 mark for any reference to the fact that Charlie saved her life when confronted by polar bears. *AF3 (1 mark)*

7 Award 1 mark for an explanation that Helen values Charlie for saving her life/scaring away polar bears. *AF3 (1 mark)*

8 Award 2 marks for inclusion of three or 1 mark for inclusion of two of the following: she was unsupported, she pulled her own sled, she was on foot, she had no warning of ice conditions. *AF2 (1–2 marks)*

9 Award 1 mark for an explanation that this shows that another famous explorer considered Helen's achievement to be remarkable. *AF6 (1 mark)*

10 Award 1 mark for reference to the fact that as the only expedition that year she had no warning of the ice conditions. *AF3 (1 mark)*

Section 2: "Roald Amundsen"

11 Award 1 mark for a brief explanation that he had been beaten to the North Pole, his original destination. *AF3 (1 mark)*

12 Award 1 mark for a brief explanation that Amundsen did not want to alert Scott to his intention to beat him to the South Pole. *AF3 (1 mark)*

13 Award 1 mark (up to a maximum of 2) for each reason given from: he did not want to be seen by Scott; he had a better route/faster route. *AF3 (1–2 marks)*

14 Award 3 marks for a response of "yes" or "no" with a fully explained reason making use of at least two well-elaborated points. Award 2 marks for at least two well explained points without as much elaboration. Award 1 mark for a single point with some explanation or two or more points without any explanation. *AF7 (1–3 marks)*

Section 3: "Scott of the Antarctic"

15 Award 1 mark for each reason given from: they had no dogs to pull their sledges (or they had to pull their own sledges); they were slowed down by the extra weight of fossils they had collected. *AF3 (1–2 marks)*

16 Award 1 mark for reference to Scott's final diary entry. *AF3 (1 mark)*

17 Award 2 marks for an explanation which includes reference to the cold/icy conditions at the Pole and reference to Scott's disappointment at arriving after Amundsen. Award 1 mark for reference to just one of the above points. *AF3 (1–2 marks)*

18 Award 2 marks for all the correct pairings of: reindeer fur – sleeping bags (given); sledges – to transport supplies; diary – to record thoughts and feelings; fossils – to help with research; photographs – evidence of expedition. Award 1 mark for two correct pairings (in addition to that given). *AF3 (1–2 marks)*

19 Award 1 mark for an explanation that the questions and answers help the reader to locate information with greater ease and/or help the text to focus on important information. *AF4 (1 mark)*

Section 4: "Explorer"

20 Award 1 mark for any indication that the cat is feeling what the snow is like. *AF3 (1 mark)*

21 Award 2 marks for a fuller explanation which makes reference to the cat being
    allowed to play on the snow without being told to "get off". There should also be
    an indication that the snow is unfamiliar and the cat can feel how cold the snow   *AF3*
    is. Award 1 mark for the first explanation only.   *(1–2 marks)*

22 Award 2 marks for a response which refers to the fact that snow is very cold
    and that because the cat's paws would sink into the snow a little, either this
    made the progress slow or the progress is slowed because the cat tests   *AF5*
    the snow. Award 1 mark for only one of the above.   *(1–2 marks)*

23 Award 2 marks for an explanation that this style breaks down the cat's movements
    into sections and matches the cat's stop-start movements as it explores the snow.   *AF4*
    Award 1 mark for an explanation which only covers one of the above points.   *(1–2 marks)*

24 Award 2 marks for an explanation which makes a contrast between the fresh,
    probably untouched snow at the start of the poem and the snow covered with
    the paw marks of the cat at the end of the poem. Award 1 mark for a brief   *AF3*
    response that the snow now has paw marks/tracks across it.   *(1–2 marks)*

Section 5: The whole booklet

25 Award 1 mark for each of the following responses with or without explanation:
    it is darker (because the sun stays below the horizon in the Antarctic winter);   *AF3*
    it is colder.   *(1–2 marks)*

26 Award 1 mark for an explanation that the table summarises information and/or
    that it makes it easier for the reader to view basic facts.   *AF4 (1 mark)*

27 Award 3 marks for a fuller explanation which includes at least three of the
    following points: some people find it exciting/fascinating to put themselves in
    danger/to push themselves to their limits; it is a challenging place to go to
    because of the very cold temperatures and the dangers from the weather and
    animals; it is an exciting place because of the danger; they are very beautiful
    places because of the snow and the interesting wildlife; it is fascinating because
    these places are largely untouched by humans. Award 2 marks for a response
    which includes two of the points and award 1 mark for a response which   *AF7*
    includes just one point.   *(1–3 marks)*

28 Award 1 mark for each correct selection from the choices below:

	Advantage	Disadvantage
North Pole	warmer climate (given)	the ice is floating; the ice is moving; the ice could melt in summer; thinner ice could crack; dark winters; polar bears
South Pole	there are bases there; it's on land; the ice isn't moving; the ice is very thick and won't crack; no polar bears	very cold all year round; dark winters; altitude makes it more difficult

AF3
(1–3 marks)

29 Award 1 mark for a correct explanation for each part of the booklet.
    "Pole to Pole"   to provide background information about the polar regions/to
                            demonstrate the challenging environments the polar regions represent.

"Polar Dream" to show that female explorers are capable of meeting the most demanding challenges/to show that polar exploration is still very demanding and challenging even though the poles were reached last century.

"Explorer" poem to put the term "exploration" into a more familiar context/to show that exploration does not just mean going to extreme places. *AF6 (1–3 marks)*

30 Award 3 marks for a fuller explanation that makes reference to the text and includes at least three of the following points: a polar explorer having to rise to the challenge in a similar way to the cat taking its first steps in the snow; the polar regions are different from anywhere else on Earth, just as the snow is different for the cat; movement is cautious for the cat, just as it must be for a polar explorer and the snow is "slow and cold" for both the cat and a polar explorer; both the cat and the polar explorer leave tracks in the snow. Award 2 marks for a response which makes two of the above points. Award 1 mark for a response which makes very simple points without comparison or elaboration. *AF3 (1–3 marks)*

The following table shows the breakdown of marks for each Assessment Focus in the Reading Test for Set B. Using the Mark Schemes, total the number of marks your child has scored against each Assessment Focus. This will provide you with a good idea of areas of strength and areas for development in their comprehension skills.

	Max Score	Score
AF2	6	
AF3	28	
AF4	4	
AF5	2	
AF6	4	
AF7	6	

Writing Test Papers Advice and Mark Scheme

There are four elements to the Writing Test:
1   Long Writing Test
2   Short Writing Test
3   Handwriting (incorporated in the Long Writing Test)
4   Spelling

The Long and Short Writing Test and the handwriting are covered by six Mark Strands (A to F). Each Strand is divided into a number of Bands. When a SATs paper is marked the marker decides, from a range of statements, into which Band a piece of writing falls. In the Mark Scheme, the statements have been turned into questions which your child and you can answer together.

It is important to read the piece of writing at least twice before you attempt to apply it to any of the Bands. Reading the text will enable you to gain a good, general feel for the content and quality.

Using the grids for each Mark Strand, you should be able to build up a picture of the Bands within which your child is working. You may notice that your child's Band for grammar and punctuation is different from their Band for "organising" or "telling" the story. It is possible to achieve different Bands for each of these Strands.

If your child is producing writing that falls within the final Band of each Mark Scheme Strand with some consistency, then it is likely that they are working at a standard of high level 5 or beyond. It is also possible that, for writing, they could be classed as Gifted or Talented by their school.

The Mark Scheme Strands show what is needed to achieve each Band. By analysing writing with your child in such detail, you will both be able to see what they do well and where their writing needs to develop. Use the questions in each Band as targets and guidance when your child is next planning and writing another text.

Familiarity with the requirements of the Writing Test are very important and targeting specific areas will develop your child's writing skills.

Administering the Writing Tests

Your child should be provided with lined paper and a pen or pencil with which to write.

For the Long Test they should be reminded that their handwriting will also be assessed. They will have 45 minutes in total. The task may be read to them and they should then aim to spend approximately 10 minutes planning and 35 minutes writing.

For the Short Test they will have 20 minutes in total, of which approximately 5 minutes should be used for planning time.

Set A and B Long Writing Test Strand A – sentence structure and punctuation

How well have you used sentences and punctuation?	Set A	Set B
Are many of your ideas and sentences very simple or linked by "and/so" or "then"?	Yes ☐ No ☐	Yes ☐ No ☐
Do you use capital letters and full stops for some sentences?	Yes ☐ No ☐	Yes ☐ No ☐

AWARD 1 MARK IF THIS IS THE BEST DESCRIPTION OF YOUR WRITING.

	Set A	Set B
Do your sentences have a correct basic grammatical structure (e.g. do subjects and verbs agree)?	Yes ☐ No ☐	Yes ☐ No ☐
Have you used simple joining words such as "and/but/or/because"?	Yes ☐ No ☐	Yes ☐ No ☐
Have you used simple descriptive phrases (e.g. "a big door", "she walked slowly")?	Yes ☐ No ☐	Yes ☐ No ☐
Are most of your sentences punctuated correctly with full stops and capital letters, and have you used commas in lists?	Yes ☐ No ☐	Yes ☐ No ☐

AWARD 2 MARKS IF YOUR WRITING MATCHES MOST OF THIS DESCRIPTION.
AWARD 3 MARKS IF YOUR WRITING MATCHES ALL OF THIS DESCRIPTION.

	Set A	Set B
Do you have some variety of sentence structures (e.g. longer sentences, shorter sentences, statements, instructions) with good use of nouns, verbs and adjectives to elaborate your ideas?	Yes ☐ No ☐	Yes ☐ No ☐
Have you used some complex sentences (e.g. clauses linked by "so that", "although", "which")?	Yes ☐ No ☐	Yes ☐ No ☐
Are your tenses and pronouns consistent?	Yes ☐ No ☐	Yes ☐ No ☐
Have you used descriptive phrases (e.g. "an eerie silence", "hidden behind the zip")?	Yes ☐ No ☐	Yes ☐ No ☐
Have you used capital letters, full stops, question marks and exclamation marks correctly in most cases?	Yes ☐ No ☐	Yes ☐ No ☐
Have you used punctuation within sentences (e.g. commas, apostrophes, speech marks)?	Yes ☐ No ☐	Yes ☐ No ☐

AWARD 4 MARKS IF YOUR WRITING MATCHES MOST OF THIS DESCRIPTION.
AWARD 5 MARKS IF YOUR WRITING MATCHES ALL OF THIS DESCRIPTION.

	Set A	Set B
Are your sentences varied in length and structure?	Yes ☐ No ☐	Yes ☐ No ☐
Have you used descriptive phrases and/or subordinate clauses to build up detail and interest?	Yes ☐ No ☐	Yes ☐ No ☐
Are your sentences (including complex sentences) mostly grammatically correct?	Yes ☐ No ☐	Yes ☐ No ☐
Have you used a variety of connectives?	Yes ☐ No ☐	Yes ☐ No ☐
Have you correctly used capital letters, full stops, question marks and exclamation marks in almost all cases?	Yes ☐ No ☐	Yes ☐ No ☐
Have you used punctuation within sentences (dashes, brackets, colons, including the punctuation of speech) and is this used correctly in most cases?	Yes ☐ No ☐	Yes ☐ No ☐

AWARD 6 MARKS IF YOUR WRITING MATCHES MOST OF THIS DESCRIPTION.
AWARD 7 MARKS IF YOUR WRITING MATCHES ALL OF THIS DESCRIPTION.

	Set A	Set B
Have you effectively used a wide range of structures to give your writing impact? Does the use of appropriate phrasing and sentencing allow the writing to convey subtle shades of meaning?	Yes ☐ No ☐	Yes ☐ No ☐
Is a wide range of punctuation used as appropriate to the structure of the sentences?	Yes ☐ No ☐	Yes ☐ No ☐
Is all punctuation accurate?	Yes ☐ No ☐	Yes ☐ No ☐

AWARD 8 MARKS IF YOUR WRITING MATCHES ALL OF THIS DESCRIPTION.

Maximum marks for this Strand: 8.

Set A and B Long Writing Test Strand B – text structure and organisation

How effectively have you structured and organised your writing?	Set A	Set B
Does your writing rely on simple connectives to show the relationship between events (e.g. "one day", "and/then", "suddenly...")?	Yes ☐ No ☐	Yes ☐ No ☐
Have you sequenced the events in a sensible order?	Yes ☐ No ☐	Yes ☐ No ☐

AWARD 1 MARK IF THIS IS THE BEST DESCRIPTION OF YOUR WRITING.

	Set A	Set B
Is there some indication that your ideas have been organised (e.g. some grouping of ideas or sentences; beginning or end section may be a separate paragraph)?	Yes ☐ No ☐	Yes ☐ No ☐
Do you have simple but coherent relationship between ideas (e.g. time markers such as "before", "as soon as", "an hour later")?	Yes ☐ No ☐	Yes ☐ No ☐
Do you maintain simple links to avoid confusion (e.g. clear use of pronouns such as "I", "she", "they")?	Yes ☐ No ☐	Yes ☐ No ☐

AWARD 2 MARKS IF YOUR WRITING MATCHES MOST OF THIS DESCRIPTION.
AWARD 3 MARKS IF YOUR WRITING MATCHES ALL OF THIS DESCRIPTION.

	Set A	Set B
Does your writing have a suitable opening?	Yes ☐ No ☐	Yes ☐ No ☐
Does your writing have clearly defined beginning, middle and end sections?	Yes ☐ No ☐	Yes ☐ No ☐
Are the events in your writing logically organised (e.g. chronologically)?	Yes ☐ No ☐	Yes ☐ No ☐
Have you signalled time/space relationships between events (e.g. "during the following afternoon", "to the left of the spacious pocket")?	Yes ☐ No ☐	Yes ☐ No ☐
Are your sentences grouped to distinguish e.g. action, description or dialogue?	Yes ☐ No ☐	Yes ☐ No ☐
Have you used paragraphs to mark the beginning, main events and ending?	Yes ☐ No ☐	Yes ☐ No ☐
Have you used details of setting/context to develop the plot or ideas?	Yes ☐ No ☐	Yes ☐ No ☐

AWARD 4 MARKS IF YOUR WRITING MATCHES MOST OF THIS DESCRIPTION.
AWARD 5 MARKS IF YOUR WRITING MATCHES ALL OF THIS DESCRIPTION.

	Set A	Set B
Is your writing well organised and convincingly structured?	Yes ☐ No ☐	Yes ☐ No ☐
Have you achieved controlled and interesting movement through the text (e.g. flashback, reference to events that follow)?	Yes ☐ No ☐	Yes ☐ No ☐
Does your writing have variety in the relationships between ideas (e.g. contrasts in mood or pacing)?	Yes ☐ No ☐	Yes ☐ No ☐
Are these relationships between ideas signalled in a variety of ways (e.g. a variety of connectives, adverbial phrases)?	Yes ☐ No ☐	Yes ☐ No ☐
Does the relationship between the paragraphs add to the cohesiveness of your text?	Yes ☐ No ☐	Yes ☐ No ☐
Have you used paragraphs confidently?	Yes ☐ No ☐	Yes ☐ No ☐

AWARD 6 MARKS IF YOUR WRITING MATCHES MOST OF THIS DESCRIPTION.
AWARD 7 MARKS IF YOUR WRITING MATCHES ALL OF THIS DESCRIPTION.

	Set A	Set B
Has your text been organised to achieve a particular effect?	Yes ☐ No ☐	Yes ☐ No ☐
Is your story line or idea well developed so that complications are convincingly resolved?	Yes ☐ No ☐	Yes ☐ No ☐
Are the various elements of your text drawn together to make a convincing conclusion?	Yes ☐ No ☐	Yes ☐ No ☐
Do you have a variety in the length and structure of individual paragraphs which add to the overall effect of your text?	Yes ☐ No ☐	Yes ☐ No ☐

AWARD 8 MARKS IF YOUR WRITING MATCHES ALL OF THIS DESCRIPTION.

Maximum marks for this Strand: 8.

Set A Long Writing Test Strand C – composition and effect – "A Peculiar Incident"

How effectively have you told the story?

Does your writing attempt to tell a story?	Yes ☐ No ☐
Does your writing have the elements of a simple story, i.e. two or more related events; one or more characters?	Yes ☐ No ☐
Have you made some attempt to interest the reader?	Yes ☐ No ☐

AWARD 1 MARK IF YOUR WRITING MATCHES MOST OF THIS DESCRIPTION.
AWARD 2 MARKS IF YOUR WRITING MATCHES ALL OF THIS DESCRIPTION.

Does your writing attempt to tell a story related to the starting point?	Yes ☐ No ☐
Do you have a beginning and a sequence of events?	Yes ☐ No ☐
Have you made an attempt to distinguish between characters (e.g. through what they say or do)?	Yes ☐ No ☐
Have you included some details designed to create interest, humour or suspense?	Yes ☐ No ☐
Does your story have a simple ending?	Yes ☐ No ☐

AWARD 3 MARKS IF YOUR WRITING MATCHES SOME OF THIS DESCRIPTION.
AWARD 4 MARKS IF YOUR WRITING MATCHES MOST OF THIS DESCRIPTION.
AWARD 5 MARKS IF YOUR WRITING MATCHES ALL OF THIS DESCRIPTION.

Is your story reasonably well paced?	Yes ☐ No ☐
Does the ending relate to the main plot?	Yes ☐ No ☐
Is there significant interaction between your characters (e.g. through dialogue)?	Yes ☐ No ☐
Is there some development of your characters through what they say or do?	Yes ☐ No ☐
Have you included details to help the reader (e.g. about the setting of the story or the characters)?	Yes ☐ No ☐

AWARD 6 MARKS IF YOUR WRITING MATCHES SOME OF THIS DESCRIPTION.
AWARD 7 MARKS IF YOUR WRITING MATCHES MOST OF THIS DESCRIPTION.
AWARD 8 MARKS IF YOUR WRITING MATCHES ALL OF THIS DESCRIPTION.

Have you used interesting story devices, e.g. does it start with dialogue or in the middle of a dramatic event? Does it include a sub-plot or a "twist"?	Yes ☐ No ☐
Is your ending convincing?	Yes ☐ No ☐
Have you engaged and kept the reader's interest (e.g. through suspense, lively characterisation, comments on events)?	Yes ☐ No ☐
Are your events, description and dialogue suitably interwoven?	Yes ☐ No ☐
Is Standard English used, or colloquialism or dialect used only for effect (e.g. in dialogue)?	Yes ☐ No ☐
Is your writing a convincing story type (e.g. mystery, traditional tale)?	Yes ☐ No ☐

AWARD 9 MARKS IF YOUR WRITING MATCHES SOME OF THIS DESCRIPTION.
AWARD 10 MARKS IF YOUR WRITING MATCHES MOST OF THIS DESCRIPTION.
AWARD 11 MARKS IF YOUR WRITING MATCHES ALL OF THIS DESCRIPTION.

Does your story engage and keep the reader's interest throughout?	
Do you draw the reader into the story through the use of various devices (e.g. imagery, metaphor and simile)?	Yes ☐ No ☐
Does your story have a theme (controlling idea) as well as a convincing plot?	Yes ☐ No ☐
Is there an interplay between characters and events?	Yes ☐ No ☐
Do your characters develop or change as a result of the story (e.g. by facing conflict or solving problems)?	Yes ☐ No ☐
Are characters given substance according to their importance to the theme or plot?	Yes ☐ No ☐
Have you drawn all elements together to make a satisfying conclusion?	Yes ☐ No ☐

AWARD 12 MARKS IF YOUR WRITING MATCHES ALL OF THIS DESCRIPTION.

Maximum marks for this Strand: 12.

Set B Long Writing Test Strand C – composition and effect – "The 2-in-1 Super Coat"

How effectively have you written the report?

Does your writing attempt to report about the product?	Yes ☐ No ☐
Does your writing have the elements of a simple report, i.e. basic information about one or more key points?	Yes ☐ No ☐
Have you made some attempt to interest the reader?	Yes ☐ No ☐

AWARD 1 MARK IF YOUR WRITING MATCHES MOST OF THIS DESCRIPTION.
AWARD 2 MARKS IF YOUR WRITING MATCHES ALL OF THIS DESCRIPTION.

Have you attempted to relate your report to the starting point?	Yes ☐ No ☐
Do you have a beginning and a sequence of points?	Yes ☐ No ☐
Have you made an attempt to distinguish between different features?	Yes ☐ No ☐
Have you included some details designed to create interest?	Yes ☐ No ☐
Does your report have a simple ending?	Yes ☐ No ☐

AWARD 3 MARKS IF YOUR WRITING MATCHES SOME OF THIS DESCRIPTION.
AWARD 4 MARKS IF YOUR WRITING MATCHES MOST OF THIS DESCRIPTION.
AWARD 5 MARKS IF YOUR WRITING MATCHES ALL OF THIS DESCRIPTION.

Is your report reasonably well paced?	Yes ☐ No ☐
Does the ending relate to the rest of the report?	Yes ☐ No ☐
Have you made links between various points?	Yes ☐ No ☐
Is there some development of the points you make (e.g. reasons)?	Yes ☐ No ☐
Have you included details to help the reader (e.g. about the background to the report or by comparison with familiar items)?	Yes ☐ No ☐

AWARD 6 MARKS IF YOUR WRITING MATCHES SOME OF THIS DESCRIPTION.
AWARD 7 MARKS IF YOUR WRITING MATCHES MOST OF THIS DESCRIPTION.
AWARD 8 MARKS IF YOUR WRITING MATCHES ALL OF THIS DESCRIPTION.

Have you used devices such as description, evaluation and justification?	Yes ☐ No ☐
Is your ending convincing?	Yes ☐ No ☐
Have you engaged and kept the reader's interest (e.g. through interesting points, lively commentary)?	Yes ☐ No ☐
Are your ideas, opinions and evidence suitably interwoven?	Yes ☐ No ☐
Have you included positive points and suggestions for improvement?	Yes ☐ No ☐

AWARD 9 MARKS IF YOUR WRITING MATCHES SOME OF THIS DESCRIPTION.
AWARD 10 MARKS IF YOUR WRITING MATCHES MOST OF THIS DESCRIPTION.
AWARD 11 MARKS IF YOUR WRITING MATCHES ALL OF THIS DESCRIPTION.

Does your report engage and keep the reader's interest throughout?	Yes ☐ No ☐
Do you draw the reader into the report through the use of various devices (e.g. imagery, metaphor and simile)?	Yes ☐ No ☐
Have you commented on the product from differing points of view (e.g. "I would use this feature although others may find it frustrating …")?	Yes ☐ No ☐
Are all of your points elaborated and justified in your writing?	Yes ☐ No ☐
Have you written an effective conclusion which summarises the report and/or makes a direct appeal to the reader?	Yes ☐ No ☐

AWARD 12 MARKS IF YOUR WRITING MATCHES ALL OF THIS DESCRIPTION.

Maximum marks for this Strand: 12.

Set A and B Short Writing Test Strand D – sentence structure, punctuation and text organisation

How well have you organised your writing and used grammar and punctuation? Set A   Set B

	Set A	Set B
Are many of your ideas and sentences very simple or linked by "and/so" or "then"?	Yes ☐ No ☐	Yes ☐ No ☐
Is there some connection between your sentences (e.g. pronouns such as "he" or "it" referring back to objects or participants already encountered)?	Yes ☐ No ☐	Yes ☐ No ☐
Do you use capital letters and full stops for some sentences?	Yes ☐ No ☐	Yes ☐ No ☐

AWARD 1 MARK IF THIS IS THE BEST DESCRIPTION OF YOUR WRITING.

	Set A	Set B
Have you used simple adjectives (e.g. "it was fun", "I liked it")?	Yes ☐ No ☐	Yes ☐ No ☐
Have you made an attempt to organise the information into different areas?	Yes ☐ No ☐	Yes ☐ No ☐
Do your sentences have a correct basic grammatical structure (e.g. do subjects and verbs agree)?	Yes ☐ No ☐	Yes ☐ No ☐
Have you used simple joining words such as "and/but/or/if"?	Yes ☐ No ☐	Yes ☐ No ☐
Do you use simple statements and simple instruction forms (e.g. "he has a clown's nose", "don't drive so fast")?	Yes ☐ No ☐	Yes ☐ No ☐
Are most of your sentences punctuated correctly with full stops and capital letters, and have you used commas in lists?	Yes ☐ No ☐	Yes ☐ No ☐

AWARD 2 MARKS IF THIS IS THE BEST DESCRIPTION OF YOUR WRITING.

	Set A	Set B
Is your information mainly organised into suitable sections?	Yes ☐ No ☐	Yes ☐ No ☐
Do you have some variety of sentence structures (e.g. longer sentences, shorter sentences, statements, instructions) with good use of nouns, verbs and adjectives to elaborate your ideas?	Yes ☐ No ☐	Yes ☐ No ☐
Are your tenses and pronouns consistent?	Yes ☐ No ☐	Yes ☐ No ☐
Have you used capital letters, full stops, question marks and exclamation marks correctly in most cases?	Yes ☐ No ☐	Yes ☐ No ☐
Have you used punctuation within sentences (e.g. commas, apostrophes)?	Yes ☐ No ☐	Yes ☐ No ☐

AWARD 3 MARKS IF THIS IS THE BEST DESCRIPTION OF YOUR WRITING.

	Set A	Set B
Are the sections of your writing developed around the main themes of the topic?	Yes ☐ No ☐	Yes ☐ No ☐
Is similar content grouped together (e.g. in paragraphs or under headings)?	Yes ☐ No ☐	Yes ☐ No ☐
Are your sentences varied in length and structure?	Yes ☐ No ☐	Yes ☐ No ☐
Have you used a variety of connectives?	Yes ☐ No ☐	Yes ☐ No ☐
Are almost all of your sentences grammatically correct?	Yes ☐ No ☐	Yes ☐ No ☐
Have you used a range of punctuation in your writing (including punctuation within sentences) and has it almost always been used correctly?	Yes ☐ No ☐	Yes ☐ No ☐

AWARD 4 MARKS IF THIS IS THE BEST DESCRIPTION OF YOUR WRITING.

Maximum marks for this Strand: 4.

Set A and B Short Writing Test Strand E – composition and effect

How effectively have you written the shorter task?	Set A	Set B
Does your writing attempt to give information?	Yes ☐ No ☐	Yes ☐ No ☐
Does your writing include some statements or instructions, but assumes that the reader already knows the background?	Yes ☐ No ☐	Yes ☐ No ☐

AWARD 1 MARK IF THIS IS THE BEST DESCRIPTION OF YOUR WRITING.

	Set A	Set B
Does your writing attempt to give information related to the starting point?	Yes ☐ No ☐	Yes ☐ No ☐
Have you clearly separated individual statements or instructions from each other (e.g. starting on a new line)?	Yes ☐ No ☐	Yes ☐ No ☐
Have you included some details designed to give a clear picture or create interest for the reader (e.g. 'It has a long, twisting slide', 'Cars sit bumper to bumper')?	Yes ☐ No ☐	Yes ☐ No ☐
Does your writing show some understanding of what readers need to know?	Yes ☐ No ☐	Yes ☐ No ☐

AWARD 2 MARKS IF YOUR WRITING MATCHES MOST OF THIS DESCRIPTION.
AWARD 3 MARKS IF YOUR WRITING MATCHES ALL OF THIS DESCRIPTION.

	Set A	Set B
Have you addressed the reader directly (e.g. 'You will really enjoy it')?	Yes ☐ No ☐	Yes ☐ No ☐
Does your writing give a fairly clear picture of the subject and the circumstances (e.g. 'the train is for children everywhere', 'cycling is more convenient in traffic')?	Yes ☐ No ☐	Yes ☐ No ☐
Does your writing give an appropriate amount of information (i.e. not too little or too much)?	Yes ☐ No ☐	Yes ☐ No ☐
Are descriptive phrases used for detail and clarity to help the reader (e.g. 'each brightly coloured carriage has a different activity')?	Yes ☐ No ☐	Yes ☐ No ☐
Have you attempted to give the reader significant and helpful details (e.g. 'You can use the Fun-tastic Express at a nearby major town or city', 'Bicycles do not cause pollution of the environment')?	Yes ☐ No ☐	Yes ☐ No ☐
Are the points you make sequenced appropriately?	Yes ☐ No ☐	Yes ☐ No ☐

AWARD 4 MARKS IF YOUR WRITING MATCHES MOST OF THIS DESCRIPTION.
AWARD 5 MARKS IF YOUR WRITING MATCHES ALL OF THIS DESCRIPTION.

	Set A	Set B
Have you engaged the reader's interest directly (e.g. through lively imaginative touches, a convincing picture of the situation)?	Yes ☐ No ☐	Yes ☐ No ☐
Have you included additional details to increase the reader's understanding and/or enjoyment of the writing?	Yes ☐ No ☐	Yes ☐ No ☐
Do you have a suitable balance between conciseness and detail (i.e. good detail but used precisely to make or elaborate a point)?	Yes ☐ No ☐	Yes ☐ No ☐
Is the tone of your writing consistent (e.g. friendly/firm but clear)?	Yes ☐ No ☐	Yes ☐ No ☐
Does your writing conform to the conventions of the type of text you have been asked to write (e.g. a persuasive letter)?	Yes ☐ No ☐	Yes ☐ No ☐
Is your writing set out appropriately (e.g. using headings or paragraphs with relevant information grouped into these sections)?	Yes ☐ No ☐	Yes ☐ No ☐

AWARD 6 MARKS IF YOUR WRITING MATCHES MOST OF THIS DESCRIPTION.
AWARD 7 MARKS IF YOUR WRITING MATCHES ALL OF THIS DESCRIPTION.

	Set A	Set B
Does your writing engage and keep the reader's interest throughout?	Yes ☐ No ☐	Yes ☐ No ☐
Does your writing read like a text in the style required by the task?	Yes ☐ No ☐	Yes ☐ No ☐
Have you adapted and shaped the content of your writing for effect?	Yes ☐ No ☐	Yes ☐ No ☐

AWARD 8 MARKS IF YOUR WRITING MATCHES ALL OF THIS DESCRIPTION.

Maximum marks for this Strand: 8.

Handwriting Mark Scheme

Set A and B Handwriting Strand F – assessed on the Long Test only

Handwriting is assessed for legibility and fluency in the Long Writing Test. You should judge the legibility and the clarity of the handwriting throughout the piece. Additionally, you should decide whether letters are correctly formed and have an appropriate size. The Mark Scheme Bands for handwriting are given below along with handwriting examples.

How neatly have you written during the longer task?   Set A   Set B

	Set A		Set B	
Is your handwriting legible?	Yes ☐	No ☐	Yes ☐	No ☐
Are most of your letters of similar size (e.g. h, k, l and g, p, y) and the correct size?	Yes ☐	No ☐	Yes ☐	No ☐
Is your spacing between most letters regular?	Yes ☐	No ☐	Yes ☐	No ☐

AWARD 1 MARK IF THIS IS THE BEST DESCRIPTION OF YOUR HANDWRITING.

Band F1 example: It's   great   to   play   on   bikes daily

	Set A		Set B	
Are your letters the right size most of the time?	Yes ☐	No ☐	Yes ☐	No ☐
Is your writing joined most of the time?	Yes ☐	No ☐	Yes ☐	No ☐
Have you used appropriate spacing between words and letters?	Yes ☐	No ☐	Yes ☐	No ☐

AWARD 2 MARKS IF THIS IS THE BEST DESCRIPTION OF YOUR HANDWRITING.

Band F2 example: It's great to play on bikes daily.

	Set A		Set B	
Is your writing joined and legible throughout the text?	Yes ☐	No ☐	Yes ☐	No ☐
Is your joined writing fluent (i.e. do the letter joins seem to "flow" evenly)?	Yes ☐	No ☐	Yes ☐	No ☐
Is the space between your letters and words even?	Yes ☐	No ☐	Yes ☐	No ☐
Are you developing a personal style in handwriting?	Yes ☐	No ☐	Yes ☐	No ☐

AWARD 3 MARKS IF THIS IS THE BEST DESCRIPTION OF YOUR HANDWRITING.

Band F3 example: It's great to play on bikes daily.

Maximum marks for this Strand: 3.

Once you have decided into which Band the handwriting falls, the score should be added to the total for the other writing tasks. These include the Spelling Test. Enter each Strand's score into the marking grid on page 30.

Sample marking of the Set A Long Writing Test – "A Peculiar Incident"

Strand A – sentence structure and punctuation
How well have you used sentences and punctuation?

This writing has a variety of long and short sentences with a range of structures including complex sentences (e.g. ... *I remembered the screams and people jumping into the water ...*). The writer uses descriptive phrases (e.g. ... *floating in a large white rowing boat in the middle of the ocean ...*) to build detail and add interest. The sentences are grammatically correct, and use connectives and a range of punctuation correctly (including punctuation within sentences). A wider range of connectives and a demonstration of knowledge of the use of more punctuation marks would help this writing to achieve a higher mark than the 6 marks it merits.

(6 marks)

Strand B – text structure and organisation
How effectively have you structured and organised your writing?

The writing is well organised and has a convincing structure with strong beginning, middle and end sections. The flow of the story is well controlled and the writer takes the characters from one setting to another very effectively. There is good variety in the relationships between ideas and these are demonstrated through changes in pace (floating on the sea followed by the storm) and mood (fear of the situation followed by the sombre memories of the cries and the bodies). The relationship between the confidently used paragraphs helps to make this a very cohesive piece of writing. Greater use of connectives and adverbial phrases would enhance the writing and take it beyond the 6 marks it merits.

(6 marks)

Strand C – composition and effect
How effectively have you written the story?

This story has an interesting "peculiar incident" with the characters taken back in time. This is then cleverly explained by the twist in the effective ending. Good description of events and an element of suspense keep the reader's interest throughout and all features of the story are suitably interwoven (e.g. use of speech to tell the reader about events). Greater characterisation, a demonstration of the use of devices such as simile and metaphor, and reference to the personal emotions of the narrator would improve the writing, which merits 9 marks.

(9 marks awarded)

Strand F – handwriting
How neatly have you written during the longer task?

The majority of the letters are the correct size, although there is little inconsistency in this aspect as well as in the spacing of words. This handwriting receives 2 marks despite the writer having developed a personal style.

Varied sentence structure.

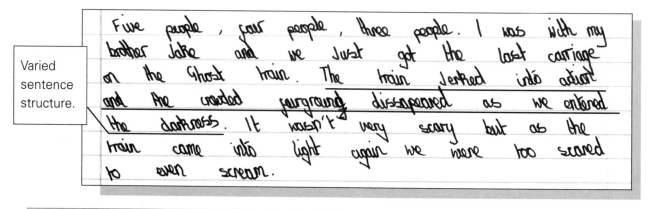

There were no other carriages and no other people. We were floating in a large white rowing boat in the middle of the ocean.

"Titanic", whispered Jake his eyes full of fear "Titanic", he repeated more slowly.

"Don't be so ridicu..." I stopped as I read a sign on the wooden seat opposite me. I remembered the screams and people jumping into the water. I remembered the bodies and cries just like in the film. Then I remembered the titanic sinking into the icey water.

Now it was daylight and we sat in the life boat. The wind was getting stronger and we were getting colder. We shouted for help but it was no use ... the waves got bigger and bigger. Suddenly a big wave came onto us. I closed my eyes and I heard a bang as our boat snapped in two.

I opened my eyes and heard another bang as our carriage bumped into the one in front. We were back at the fairground, we got of the ride and walked to mum and dad. "Look at you two". Soaked wet through. "Was that fun?" questioned dad. Neither of us answered " Too scared to talk then?" he laughed.

When we got home we sat in front of the television and watched a programme about the titanic. "Your great grandad and his sister were on the titanic you know it would have been his birthday this week, he used to work rides at a fairground." Nobody knew if they got to a lifeboat or not".

Nobody knew except me and my brother.

Annotations in margin:

- Descriptive phrase.
- Capitalisation of proper noun not used.
- Simple connectives.
- Clear, main event.
- Confident use of paragraphs.
- Colloquial phrasing.
- Explanatory twist in effective ending.

Sample marking of the Set A Short Writing Test – "Fun-tastic Express"

Strand D – sentence structure, punctuation and text organisation
How well have you organised your writing and used grammar and punctuation?

This writing develops the theme coherently and the content is well organised into distinct paragraphs. A variety of sentence structure and length has been used and devices to connect parts of sentences have been used creatively (e.g. ...*With tunnels and loops, this has to be the best ride ever*). The sentences are mostly grammatically correct, and a range of punctuation has been used correctly and to good effect. This writing merits 4 marks.

(4 marks)

Strand E – composition and effect
How effectively have you written the shorter task?

The reader is immediately alerted to the fact that this writing is about something special (*Thrilling, fast, exciting and fun!*) The writing addresses the reader directly and the pace adds to the general feeling that the writer is very enthusiastic about the train. There is a balance between conciseness and detail (greater detail about the rollercoaster, less detail about the other attractions) and, apart from a repetition of the list of attractions, there is no unnecessary information. There is a consistently friendly tone and the writing certainly conforms to the conventions of an informative piece.
The effect is enhanced by clear paragraphing of grouped information which provides a smooth flow to the writing. A little more information about the rollercoaster (the favourite activity) would add to the overall effect and for this reason this writing merits 6 rather than 7 marks.

(6 marks)

Thrilling, fast, exciting and fun! Come to the fun-tastic Express to have the best time ever on a train. You'll never believe that there is a magician, an adventure playground, a ball pool and a mini-rollercoaster on the train at your train station.

My favourite ride was the mini-rollercoaster. The rollercoaster comes in and out of the train in a mad kind of way. With tunnels and loops, this has to be the best ride ever. All the rides are brilliant, the ball pool pool and magician to chill out, and an adventure playground to test your strength.

You must go to this fun and exciting train. Even if you can't go on a trip on the train, why not spare a morning here? Its more fun going on the train than just reading about it. Why not come and and have the time of your life?

For your free information pack, visit your local train station now!

Sample marking of the Set B Long Writing Test – "The 2-in-1 Super Coat"

Strand A – sentence structure and punctuation
How well have you used sentences and punctuation?

The writing uses a variety of sentence structures, including complex sentences (e.g. *It has a fleece for extra warmth which can be zipped up if needed.*) There is consistent use of tense and pronouns. Some descriptive phrases are used (e.g. ... *elastic cuffs to stop draughts getting inside ...*). There is correct use of capital letters and full stops. There has been an attempt to use commas in sentences although from the two instances (one correct the other incorrect) and the lack of any other punctuation within sentences, it is not possible to say that the child knows how to use punctuation in this way. For this reason, 4 rather than 5 marks have been awarded to this writing for Strand A.   *(4 marks)*

Strand B – text structure and organisation
How effectively have you structured and organised your writing?

The opening is suitable, providing a brief overview of the context and the report. This writing has clearly defined beginning, middle and end sections. The events (the positive and negative aspects of the coat) are handled separately, and the spatial relationship between the coat and its features is touched upon (e.g. *a mobile pocket in the inside layer*). Sentences are grouped to distinguish feelings about the positive and negative aspects, and paragraphs clearly mark the beginning, middle and end sections. The context is given and this is continued throughout the writing with subtle reminders that this is a review of a product by a group of children (e.g. ... *some not so great things; ... Overall we thought ...*). The writing does not really have any variety in its structure and organisation (in the mood, apart from separate paragraphs for positive and negative aspects, or in the use of connectives). This writing therefore merits no greater than 5 marks.   *(5 marks)*

Strand C – composition and effect
How effectively have you written the report?

This report is well paced – it makes relevant points throughout and does not stray from the main theme. The ending is weak and, although related to the rest of the report, requires more (albeit brief) reference to the main points. There are clear links between various points (e.g. discussing the zip up fleece then going on to mention the outer waterproof layer ... *and both layers are made of lightweight material ...*) and points are developed (e.g. providing a reason for not liking the safety light ... *We thought it might get broken ...*). Detail to help the reader is provided through giving the context although comparison to other items (e.g. a standard coat) would enhance the report. This writing matches the descriptions to just enable it to gain 8 marks, although further examples of all of the above points would make a stronger case and a livelier, more convincing argument would take it up to 9 or 10 marks.   *(8 marks)*

Strand F – handwriting
How neatly have you written during the longer task?

Most of the letters are the correct size (although the letter f is consistently poor) and the writing is mostly joined. The spacing between words and letters is appropriate but not quite even. There is evidence of a personal style developing but this handwriting merits 2 rather than 3 marks.   *(2 marks)*

My class have been testing the new 2 in 1 super coat and we think it is very good and very useful. We have found some great things and some not so great things that could be better.

The good bits about the coat are that it is for both boys and girls. It has a fleece for extra warmth which can be zipped out if needed. The outer layer is waterproof and both layers are made of lightweight material to make it better to wear. The reflective strips mean you can be seen in the dark. Both layers have elastic cuffs to help stop draughts getting inside the coat. Finally it has a mobile pocket in the inside layer to help keep your phone safe.

The three things we thought that were not so great, were the safety light. We thought it might get broken and may add weight. Although the coat has a fixed hood, a removable one would add greater flexibility. The coat has 4 pockets in each layer with buttons but it may be better to use zips.

Overall we thought it was a good coat that could be improved with a few slight design changes.

Repetitive sentence and ideas structure.

Complex sentence.

Descriptive phrase.

Clear structure: paragraphs for good and bad features.

Clear conclusion but with little extra detail.

Sample marking of the Set B Short Writing Test – "On your Bike"

Strand D – sentence structure, punctuation and text organisation
How well have you organised your writing and used grammar and punctuation?

The sections of this writing are organised into paragraphs containing different angles on the theme. There is evidence of a good variety of sentence structures and lengths. Simple joining words are used (e.g. *if, plus, then*) and most sentences are grammatically correct. Punctuation is mostly correct and an attempt has been made at punctuation within sentences, although better use of this would enhance the writing. A further benefit would be the use of more imaginative connectives. This writing merits 2 rather than 3 marks.

(2 marks)

Strand E – composition and effect
How effectively have you written the shorter task?

The writing makes a direct appeal to its intended audience and gives a fairly clear picture of the subject and circumstances. There is an appropriate amount of information given but some reiteration of the points made in the prompt would help to take this writing into a higher band. Short descriptive phrases are in evidence (*They're quiet, and they don't pollute the environment ...; Cars pollute, bikes don't*). These points also provide significant and helpful detail for the reader, and all of the points made are sequenced properly. Unfortunately, a lack of emotion in the writing reduces the persuasive effects of the letter, which merits 4 marks.

(4 marks)

Dear Editor,
I am writing to disagree with Anne Eastwood about her saying that cycling is wrong.

Bikes am't a nuisance, they keep you fit and healthy, plus you can have a lot of fun on them.
Cycling will keep you fit, If you cycle regulary.

What is wrong with bikes?
They're quiet, and they don't pollute the environment with nasty fumes! They are safe if you wear a helmet too and ride sensibly.

If you put lots of cyclepaths down then the cyclists won't disturb drivers of cars/lorrys or trucks. Cars pollute, bikes don't.

If bikes were banned then the world would just be a polluted peice of land. Please don't ban bikes.
Yours sincerely
Michael Gibson

Spelling Test Advice, Text and Mark Scheme

Administering the Spelling Test

The Spelling Test consists of a short piece of text which should be read twice in its entirety to the child taking the test. During the first reading the child should not write anything on their answer sheet. During the second reading the reader should pause after each word to be tested (in bold type) to enable the child to write the word into the gap on their answer sheet.

The complete passages for Set A and Set B Spelling Tests are below.

Set A Spelling – "Belgian Connection"

In 1815 the Duke of Wellington **defeated** the French army of Napoleon near the **village** of Waterloo, a few kilometres from Brussels in Belgium. The Battle of Waterloo was not only **seen** as a great **victory** for the British but it also gave its name to a **central** London railway station.

Waterloo station was **opened** on 11 July 1848 by London South West Railway. Over the **following** 50 years many more parts were added as a result of the **dramatic** increase in the number of railway lines. **Between** 1902 and 1922 the station was completely rebuilt and had its **official** opening in March 1922. A Victory Arch, representing war and **peace**, was **incorporated** into the façade. This commemorated workers who died in World War I.

As the **twentieth** century came to a close, Waterloo was **enlarged** as it became London's main **connection** with the railways of Europe **through** the Channel Tunnel. The station **boasts** the largest roof area of any railway station in the UK and has shops, food outlets and even a **cinema**.

Remarkably, the station now also has a new link with Belgium. **Each** day the Eurostar **service** runs up to nine trains a day from London Waterloo to Brussels. *Information correct until 31st December 2006.

Set B Spelling – "Cool Sports"

Despite being cold and hard, ice has become **widely** used by humans for many sports.
They all **require** nerve and skill to both maintain balance and **compete** at the same time.

Ice-skating involves **propelling** yourself across ice using **special** bladed boots **known** as skates.
It is an **extremely** popular sport throughout the world and has several forms.

Speed skating involves races on a frozen **circuit** over distances of up to 10,000 **metres**. The races are much quicker than **similar** races on an athletics track. At the 1980 Winter Olympics, the speed skater Eric Heiden won five gold medals, a **feat** never previously **achieved** in the sport.

Figure skating is an event for individuals or mixed pairs. The **competitors** skate to music while **attempting** to perform a range of spectacular and **accurate** moves such as spins and jumps. They are then **judged** for technical merit, required elements and **presentation**.

Ice hockey is a team game **played** on ice. It is regarded as the fastest team sport in the world with the players hitting the puck at well over 100 km per hour. With the pace of the game and **passionate** crowds the **action** often gets very exciting and sometimes violent.

Marking the Spelling Test

After completion of the test, total up the number of words spelt correctly. This total for the Spelling Test is converted into marks that contribute to the overall level for Writing. Marks should be given as indicated.

Number of correct words	1–3	4–6	7–9	10–12	13–15	16–18	19–20
Marks	1	2	3	4	5	6	7

Marking the Tests and Assessing Levels

1   Marking the practice papers is quite simple. Just use the answers provided in this booklet for each test.

2   Make sure your child has completed all the relevant tests, e.g. Set A Reading Paper, Set A Long Writing Test Paper and Set A Spelling Test paper.

3   Add up the marks on each paper. The Reading Test Paper is marked out of 50, the Writing is marked out of 50. This gives a maximum total of 100 marks.

4   Write the marks in the corresponding table below.

Complete the grids with the scores when marking each paper.

Section	Marks available	Set A score	Set B score
Reading Scores			
Reading Test	50		
Writing Scores			
Long Writing Test – sentence structure and punctuation (Strand A)	8		
Long Writing Test – text structure and organisation (Strand B)	8		
Long Writing Test – composition and effect (Strand C)	12		
Handwriting (Strand F)	3		
Short Writing Test – sentence structure, punctuation and text organisation (Strand D)	4		
Short Writing Test – composition and effect (Strand E)	8		
Spelling Test	7		
Total score	100		

Curriculum Levels

Reading level

Below Level 3	Level 3	Level 4	Level 5	High Level 5
up to 10	11–22	23–35	36–45	46+

Writing level

Below Level 3	Level 3	Level 4	Level 5	High Level 5
up to 18	19–30	31–38	39–47	48+

Combined English level

Below Level 3	Level 3	Level 4	Level 5	High Level 5
up to 29	30–53	54–74	75–93	94+

Shared marking and target setting

Engaging your child in the marking process with you will help them to develop a greater understanding of the English Tests and, more importantly, provide them with some ownership of their learning. They will be able to see more clearly how and why certain areas have been identified for them to target for improvement.

Please note: these tests are only a guide to the level your child can achieve and cannot guarantee the same level is achieved at KS2.

How well has my child done in these tests?
The results show whether or not your child has reached the expected National Curriculum level for their age.

	Aged 7	Aged 11	Aged 14
Level 1	Below average		
Level 2 Level 2a Level 2b Level 2c	At level expected	Below average	
Level 3	Excellent	Below average	Below average
Level 4	Exceptional	At level expected	Below average
Level 5		Excellent	At level expected
Level 6		Exceptional	At level expected
Level 7			Excellent
Level 8			Exceptional

What do the levels mean?

When your child's English papers are marked, the correct marks are collated to give your child an overall score. This score is then matched to a National Curriculum level.

It is expected that the majority of 11 year old children will achieve Level 4 by the end of Year 6. However, for some children achieving Level 3 is a real success for that particular individual. A child achieving Level 5 is working at a high level, and only one percent achieve Level 6. A child who passes GCSE at grade C has achieved level 7.

Set **A**

KEY STAGE 2
Levels 3–5

Long Writing
Test Paper

English

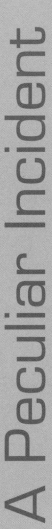
A Peculiar Incident

Long Writing Test Paper

A Peculiar Incident

Instructions:

- find a quiet place where you can sit down and complete the test paper undisturbed

- make sure you have all the necessary equipment to complete the test paper

- read the question carefully

- answer the question on lined paper

- go through and check your answer when you have finished writing

Time:

This test paper is **45 minutes** long. This includes planning and writing time. Aim to spend approximately **10 minutes** planning your writing using the planning prompts.

Check how your child has done against the mark scheme in the Instructions, Answers and Mark Scheme Booklet.

	Max. Mark	**Actual Mark**
Score	31	....

First name ....

Last name ....

A Peculiar Incident

The Ghost Train ride was more funny than spooky. That was until the moment we came out of the dark and back into the fairground. Nothing was the same. Everything had changed.

Your task is to write a story based on this idea.

You should think about these things:

1   The characters in the story.

2   What has changed.

3   What happened next.

4   The ending of the story.

Planning

Write useful words and phrases to help you develop the story. These notes will not be marked.

Beginning

Middle

End

Set B

KEY STAGE 2
Levels 3–5

Long Writing
Test Paper

English

The 2-in-1 Super Coat

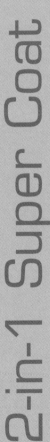

Long Writing Test Paper

The 2-in-1 Super Coat

Instructions:

- find a quiet place where you can sit down and complete the test paper undisturbed

- make sure you have all the necessary equipment to complete the test paper

- read the question carefully

- answer the question on lined paper

- go through and check your answer when you have finished writing

Time:

This test paper is **45 minutes long**. This includes planning and writing time. Aim to spend approximately **10 minutes** planning your writing using the planning prompts.

Check how your child has done against the mark scheme in the Instructions, Answers and Mark Scheme Booklet.

	Max. Mark	**Actual Mark**
Score	31	....

First name ....

Last name ....

The 2-in-1 Super Coat

Some of your class have been asked to test the new
2-in-1 Super Coat manufactured by a local company.
The company need it testing by children before they
produce their final version for sale in the shops.

The *2-in-1 Super Coat* has the following features.

1   Blue waterproof outer layer with a zip in/zip out fleece. The fleece and the outer
layer can both be worn alone or together for extra warmth and waterproofing.

2   Suitable for both boys and girls.

3   Four large single button pockets on both layers.

4   A fixed hood on the outer layer.

5   Elasticated cuffs on both layers.

6   A special mobile phone pocket inside the fleece layer.

7   Reflective strips on the back of the outer layer.

8   Lightweight material for both layers.

9   A built-in safety light on the front of the outer layer.

Your task is to write a report about the jacket for the company. You should think about
the features mentioned and say how these are good or poor design points. You can
make recommendations to the company on how you feel the jacket could be changed
before it goes on sale. Use the planning prompts to help you.

Planning

Use this page to make brief notes as you plan your ideas. These notes will not be marked.

Good features of the coat	Things that need to be improved

How will I start the report?

_____

_____

_____

How will I end the report?

_____

_____

_____

Set
B

KEY STAGE 2
Levels 3–5

Short Writing
Test Paper

English

On Your Bike

Short Writing Test Paper

On Your Bike

Instructions:

- find a quiet place where you can sit down and complete the test paper undisturbed

- make sure you have all the necessary equipment to complete the test paper

- read the question carefully

- answer the question on lined paper

- go through and check your answer when you have finished writing

Time:

This test paper is **20 minutes** long. This includes planning and writing time. Aim to spend approximately **5 minutes** planning your writing using the planning prompts.

Check how your child has done against the mark scheme in the Instructions, Answers and Mark Scheme Booklet.

	Max. Mark	**Actual Mark**
Score	12	....

First name ....

Last name ....

On Your Bike

Bicycle facts

1   Cycling is a very good form of exercise – ride a bike and keep fit.

2   Bicycles do not pollute the environment with nasty fumes.

3   Bicycles are quiet.

4   Bicycles are relatively safe if you wear a helmet and ride sensibly.

5   Cycling can be great fun.

The following letter has just been printed in your local newspaper:

Dear Editor,

I am fed up of the council building new cycle paths everywhere. I think bikes are a nuisance. Children are constantly riding up and down my street on their bikes and when I am driving I always end up having to overtake slow cyclists. Why can't the children walk and why can't grown-ups just use their cars?

I think bikes should be banned, leaving the streets for cars only. This will help everyone get to where they are going more quickly and make the world a safer place, because people will not fall off, or get knocked off, their bikes.

Yours sincerely,

Anne Eastwood

Your task is to write a letter to the newspaper persuading readers why you feel Anne Eastwood is wrong. Use the *Bicycle facts* and other information which you think should be included. Plan your work very briefly on the next page.

Planning

Make a few brief notes to help you plan your ideas. These notes will not be marked.

Points you will argue against	Evidence you will use

Set
B

KEY STAGE 2
Levels 3–5

Spelling
Test Paper

English

Cool Sports

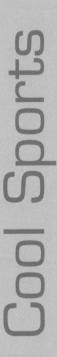

Spelling Test Paper

includes Spelling Guide for Children

Cool Sports

Instructions to parents:

- find a quiet place where you can sit down with your child

- make sure you have all the necessary equipment to complete the test paper

- read the short piece of text on page 28 of the Instructions, Answers and Mark Scheme Booklet to your child twice in its entirety

- during the first reading, your child should not write anything in this booklet

- during the second reading, pause after each word to be tested (shown in bold type), to enable your child to write the word in the gap in this booklet

- check how your child has done against the mark scheme in the Instructions, Answers and Mark Scheme Booklet

	Max.	**Number of words correct**
Score	20	....

See page 29 of the Instructions, Answers and Mark Scheme Booklet for the spelling test mark conversion chart.

First name ....

Last name ....

Cool Sports

Despite being cold and hard, ice has become _____ used by

humans for many sports. They all _____ nerve and skill to both

maintain balance and _____ at the same time.

Ice-skating involves _____ yourself across ice using

_____ bladed boots _____ as skates. It is an

_____ popular sport throughout the world and has several forms.

Speed skating involves races on a frozen _____ over distances

of up to 10,000 _____. The races are much quicker than

_____ races on an athletics track. At the 1980 Winter Olympics,

the speed skater Eric Heiden won five gold medals, a _____

never previously _____ in the sport.

Figure skating is an event for individuals or mixed pairs. The

_____ skate to music while _____ to

perform a range of spectacular and _____ moves such as spins

and jumps. They are then _____ for technical merit, required

elements and _____.

Ice hockey is a team game _____ on ice. It is regarded as the

fastest team sport in the world with the players hitting the puck at well over 100 km

per hour. With the pace of the game and _____ crowds the

_____ often gets very exciting and sometimes violent.

Spelling Guide for Children

This information will not appear on the back of an official SATs Spelling Test. It is included here to help you to improve your spelling score.

It is a good idea to practise memorising how words "look" and the letter sequences in more complex words. You need to get used to considering whether a word "looks right".

A useful way to help you to memorise a spelling is to use the routine of "Look, Cover, Write, Check".

LOOK   Look at a word and identify phonic patterns (sound patterns) or sequences of letters within the word.

COVER   Cover the word but try to memorise the spelling.

WRITE   Write the spelling down.

CHECK   Check whether the written word is spelt correctly, identify any mistakes, then try again.

Set
A

KEY STAGE 2
Levels 3–5

Spelling
Test Paper

English

Belgian Connection

Spelling Test Paper

includes Spelling Guide for Parents

Belgian Connection

Instructions to parents:

- find a quiet place where you can sit down with your child

- make sure you have all the necessary equipment to complete the test paper

- read the short piece of text on page 28 of the Instructions, Answers and Mark Scheme Booklet to your child twice in its entirety

- during the first reading, your child should not write anything in this booklet

- during the second reading, pause after each word to be tested (shown in bold type), to enable your child to write the word in the gap in this booklet

- check how your child has done against the mark scheme in the Instructions, Answers and Mark Scheme Booklet

	Max.	**Number of words correct**
Score	20	....

See page 29 of the Instructions, Answers and Mark Scheme Booklet for the spelling test mark conversion chart.

Letts

First name ....

Last name ....

Belgian Connection

In 1815 the Duke of Wellington _____ the French army of

Napoleon near the _____ of Waterloo, a few kilometres from

Brussels in Belgium.

The Battle of Waterloo was not only _____ as a great

_____ for the British but it also gave its name to a

_____ London railway station.

Waterloo station was _____ on 11 July 1848 by London South West Railway. Over the _____ 50 years many more parts were added as a result of the _____ increase in the number of railway lines.

_____ 1902 and 1922 the station was completely rebuilt and had its _____ opening in March 1922. A Victory Arch, representing war and _____ , was _____ into the façade. This commemorated workers who died in World War I.

As the _____ century came to a close, Waterloo was _____ as it became London's main _____ with the railways of Europe _____ the Channel Tunnel. The station _____ the largest roof area of any railway station in the UK and has shops, food outlets and even a _____. Remarkably, the station now also has a new link with Belgium. _____ day the Eurostar _____ runs up to nine trains a day from London Waterloo to Brussels.

Spelling Guide for Parents

This information will not appear on the back of an official SATs Spelling Test. It is included here to help you to improve your child's spelling score.

During Key Stage 2 your child should develop their skills in spelling. The Literacy Strategy sets out words that children should learn each year they are in primary school. You should check your child knows the Key Stage 2 words. Spelling is best learnt when both phonic strategies (sound) and visual strategies (recognising groups of letters) are used.

In the early stages of learning to spell, children should learn to memorise short common words, e.g. *get*, *went*. Then they should learn to match sounds to letters – this should help them to spell simple words.

As your child becomes more aware of the relationship between sounds and letters, you should help them to see that patterns exist. These include:

1   the effect of doubling the vowel, e.g. "ee" as in *sheep*, *sleep*, *freeze*

2   how certain vowels and consonants combine, e.g. "ar" as in *car*, *card*, *hard*

3   how some consonants combine to make particular sounds, e.g. "ch" as in *chain*, *choice*, *chase*

4   how a silent 'e' affects the vowel, e.g. *hop/hope*, *bit/bite*, *car/care*

5   how two vowels combine to give a particular sound, e.g. "oi" as in *oil*, *boil*, *toil*

6   how the grouping of two or more letters gives a particular sound, e.g. "igh" as in *sigh*, *high*, *slight*

7   how words that have long vowel sounds such as *journey* need to be committed to visual memory

8   how words with double consonants need to be memorised, e.g. *commented*

Please note that these are just a selection of patterns and strategies. There are more and if you have concern about your child's spelling do not hesitate to raise the issue with their teacher.

Advice for children is provided at the back of Set B Spelling Test Paper, on page 4.

Set A

KEY STAGE 2
Levels 3–5

Short Writing
Test Paper

English

Fun-tastic Express

Short Writing Test Paper

Fun-tastic Express

Instructions:

- find a quiet place where you can sit down and complete the test paper undisturbed
- make sure you have all the necessary equipment to complete the test paper
- read the question carefully
- answer the question on lined paper
- go through and check your answer when you have finished writing

Time:

This test paper is **20 minutes** long. This includes planning and writing time. Aim to spend approximately **5 minutes** planning your writing using the planning prompts.

Check how your child has done against the mark scheme in the Instructions, Answers and Mark Scheme Booklet.

	Max. Mark	**Actual Mark**
Score	12	....

First name ....

Last name ....

Fun-tastic Express

A new train providing entertainment for children as it visits major towns and cities has just started to operate. The activities on offer are:

1   a magician

2   an adventure playground

3   a ball pool

4   a mini-rollercoaster.

The Fun-tastic Express wants a display in the nearest railway station to your school.

Imagine you have been on the Fun-tastic Express and write a review of your favourite activity for the display.

Planning

Before you start, briefly consider these things. These notes will not be marked.

The activity you enjoyed most and why

Key words to describe the activity

KEY STAGE 2
Levels 3–5

Reading Booklet

English

POLAR EXPLORER

Polar Explorer

Contents

Introduction

The Arctic and Antarctic regions in general, and the North and South Poles in particular, have long intrigued explorers and adventurers.

In the early years of the twentieth century, there were determined efforts to be the first to reach the Poles and even modern explorers find new challenges in these icy wilderness areas.

In this booklet, you are given a flavour of what the polar regions of our planet are like in *Pole to Pole*. There are also articles on three polar explorers, covering the race to the South Pole and more modern polar exploration. Finally, the poem *Explorer* looks at the way a cat might explore a snow-covered garden.

Pole to Pole

The polar regions are the extremely cold areas found to the far north and south of our planet. They are considered to be among the most inhospitable places on Earth and were the last large areas on Earth to be explored.

The Arctic

The northern polar region is known as the Arctic. This is a huge ocean surrounded by land. The North Pole (the most northerly point on Earth) is in this ocean. However, it is possible to get to the North Pole on foot, because a large proportion of the ocean remains frozen all year round.

During the Arctic winter, the sun never rises and during the summer it never sets, although it remains low in the sky and is therefore very weak.

Although people live on the land at the edge of the Arctic Ocean, they do not live at the North Pole because the ice is floating and moving.

The Antarctic

The Antarctic is the southern polar region and the South Pole can be found here. Unlike the North Pole, the South Pole is completely surrounded by land.

As with the Arctic, the sun never rises during an Antarctic winter and remains close to the horizon during the summer. However, throughout the year the Antarctic remains much colder, partly due to the fact that most of the continent is high above sea level and is covered in thousands of metres of ice, rather than just a few metres as in the Arctic.

There are no native inhabitants on the Antarctic land mass, but special international treaties allow scientists from many countries to live there and undertake valuable research. Much of the information we know about the ozone layer and global warming has come from these scientists.

The following table provides a summary of some key facts about the polar regions of our planet.

	Arctic	Antarctic
Situation	Ocean surrounded by continents	Continent surrounded by oceans
Temperature in winter	–10°C to –30°C	–25°C to –70°C
Temperature in summer	0°C	–2°C to –40°C
Ice thickness	1.5 to 9 metres (floating sea ice)	2500 metres (average thickness)
Main animal life	Polar bears Whales Seals	Penguins Whales Seals
Human inhabitants	Inuits on the land surrounding the frozen ocean	Scientists from many countries

Polar Dream

Helen Thayer was born in New Zealand. She has become a world-famous adventurer, author and photographer, telling the stories of her adventures in words and pictures.

In 1988, at the age of 50, Helen decided to walk alone to the magnetic North Pole without the aid of aircraft, dog teams or snow mobiles. She was totally unsupported. She walked and skied, pulling her own 160 pound sled filled with all her supplies. Her only companion was Charlie, a black Canadian Eskimo Husky, who had been a valuable polar bear dog for the Inuit of Resolute Bay in the polar region of Northern Canada. Charlie's only job was to walk at Helen's side to protect her from polar bears. He did his job well. He saved her life at least once. They were confronted by seven polar bears, one at a time, throughout the almost month-long journey of 586 km (364 miles). Helen circumnavigated the entire magnetic North Pole area.

She began on 30 March and finished on 27 April. It was a long and lonely journey. Helen's expedition was the only one going to the magnetic North Pole in 1988, therefore she had no warning of the ice conditions which lay ahead of her.

She then wrote a book about her journey to the Pole titled *Polar Dream* with a foreword by Sir Edmund Hillary. It is the story of her faithful dog, Charlie, who travelled at her side during her journey. Charlie went home with Helen and lives with three other dogs, four goats and two donkeys. He runs daily with the Thayers, hikes and climbs mountains. He truly enjoys a life of luxury. As Helen will tell you, "What Charlie wants, Charlie gets."

Roald Amundsen

Roald Amundsen, a Norwegian, spent almost all his adult life in exploration. He was the first explorer to navigate the Northwest Passage between the Atlantic and the Pacific oceans to the north of Canada. However, he is most famous for being the first person to reach the South Pole. Yet his journey to Antarctica was almost an accident.

Amundsen was 37 years old when he decided in 1909 to make an attempt on the North Pole, which had not then been reached. But, while he was preparing for the journey, news came that the American explorer Robert Peary had arrived at the Pole. Amundsen secretly changed his plans, telling only his brother, and headed for the South Pole instead. He knew that a British expedition led by Robert Falcon Scott had already set out with the same aim, but travelling by a different route, he overtook the British party. Amundsen's five-man group set out from his base camp in October 1911 on sledges drawn by huskies on what was to be an eight-week journey. On 14 December 1911, Amundsen reached the Pole and planted the Norwegian flag there. He was about four weeks ahead of Scott.

Scott of the Antarctic

Scott of the Antarctic. Who was he?

Scott of the Antarctic is a nickname that has been given to the famous British naval officer and explorer Robert Falcon Scott. From a very early age, however, he was known as "Con" (from the name Falcon). Con joined the navy at the age of 13 and rose through the ranks over the next few years of his life. In late 1911 he led an expedition into unknown areas of Antarctica, aiming to become the first man to stand at the South Pole. On 17 January 1912, Scott reached his destination.

It's cold there. So what do you wear?

Modern polar explorers wear several layers of highly technical thermal, breathable and waterproof clothing. The fabrics used are lightweight and often very expensive. These clothes are used for sleeping too, when the explorer climbs into a specially made sleeping bag. Scott's party had none of this. They had to wear layer on layer of sweaters with woollen hats and woollen and fur mittens. Nature provided them with reindeer fur for boots and sleeping bags.

How on earth do you get to the South Pole?

With great difficulty. Even almost a hundred years later, explorers who attempt to make the South Pole on foot are often thwarted by dangerous conditions, even though they have lightweight equipment and sometimes use teams of dogs to help with the load. Imagine what it must have been like for Scott and his party. They did not have the luxury of a dog team and chose to pull their own supplies across the icy wastes of Antarctica.

So what did Scott find at the South Pole?

The following words were recorded in Scott's diary: "Great God! This is an awful place ..." Unfortunately for Scott it was not just the place itself that was awful. As his team approached the Pole they saw a speck in the distance. They got closer and realised the terrible truth – the speck was a Norwegian flag. Roald Amundsen had beaten them to the South Pole and the tracks of his dogs still lay in the snow. All Scott had to show for the journey were diary entries, photographs and 15 kilograms of fossils collected along the way.

What did Scott do next?

All he could do was turn around and lead his party back home. Luck was not on their side, however. They managed to get themselves just a few miles from relative safety but a huge blizzard and frost-bitten limbs prevented them going further. Scott wrote a final entry in his diary on 29 March, 1912 saying: "The end cannot be far." Somehow, although on the verge of death, he still managed to write letters to his loved ones. The bodies of the party were found eight months later.

Two o'clock:
Let out of the back door of the house, our cat
Is practising the snow.

The layer of white makes a small straight, crumbling cliff
Where we open the back door inwards. The cat
Sniffs at it with suspicion, learns you can just about
Pat at the flaking snow with a careful dab. Then,
A little bolder, he dints it with one whole foot
– And withdraws it, curls it as if slightly lame,

And looks down at it, oddly. The snow is
Different from anything else, not like
A rug, or a stretch of lino, or an armchair to claw upon
And be told to *Get off!*

The snow is peculiar, but not forbidden. The cat
Is welcome to go out in the snow. Does
The snow welcome the cat?
He thinks, looks, tries again.

Three paces out of the door, his white feet find
You sink a little way all of the time, it is slow and cold,
      but it
Doesn't particularly hurt. Perhaps you can even enjoy
      it as something new.
So he walks on, precisely, on the tips of very
      cautious paws ...

Half past three, the cat stretched warm indoors,
From the bedroom window we can see his explorations

– From door to fence, from fence to gate, from gate to
      wall to tree, and back,
Are long patterned tracks and trade-routes of round
      paw-marks
Which fresh snow is quietly filling.

By Alan Brownjohn

Set B

KEY STAGE 2
Levels 3–5

Reading Test
Paper

English

Polar Explorer

Reading Test Paper

includes Reading Guide for Children

Polar Explorer

Instructions:

- find a quiet place where you can sit down and complete the test paper undisturbed
- make sure you have all the necessary equipment to complete the test paper
- read the questions carefully
- answer all the questions in this booklet
- go through and check your answers when you have finished the test paper

Time:

This test paper is **1 hour** long.

You should ensure you spend **15 minutes** reading through the Reading Booklet before you begin the test. Do not worry if you have not read the whole Reading Booklet in this time, because you can (and should) look at the Reading Booklet as many times as you like during the test.

The main written part of the test should take **45 minutes**. There are several question types:

Multiple choice	you put a ring around the correct option
Short answers	requiring only a word or short phrase
Several line answers	these questions require you to write more than a single point
Explanation answers	you are required to write an answer and explain it, often in quite a lot of detail and with evidence from the text
Other answers	you may be required to draw lines connecting related words

Check how your child has done against the mark scheme in the Instructions, Answers and Mark Scheme Booklet.

Page	3	5	7	9	11	13	Max. Mark	**Actual Mark**
Score	....	....	....	....	....	....	50	....

First name _____

Last name _____

Section 1

These questions are about the text "Polar Dream" on page 6 of the Set B Reading Booklet.

Choose the correct word or group of words and put a ring around your choice.

1   Helen Thayer travelled to the magnetic North Pole by: (1 mark)

Q1

    aircraft.

    snow mobile.

    walking and skiing.

    car.

2   Charlie was a husky dog taken along on the journey to: (1 mark)

Q2

    pull the sled.

    scare away polar bears.

    enjoy the walk.

    be nice.

3   After the expedition Charlie: (1 mark)

Q3

    went back to the Inuits.

    hunted for polar bears.

    went to live with Helen.

    stayed in the Arctic.

4   Helen took a sled along with her to: *(1 mark)*

sit on.

carry her supplies.

carry rocks she found.

shelter beneath.

5   Helen wrote a book about her journey called: *(1 mark)*

Polar Dream.

Travel with Charlie.

My Journey.

My Autobiography.

6   How did Charlie prove to be an invaluable companion on Helen Thayer's journey?

(1 mark)

_____

_____

7 Why does the text tell us that *"What Charlie wants, Charlie gets"*?   *(1 mark)*

Q7

_____

_____

_____

8 List three things that made Helen's journey all the more remarkable.   *(2 marks)*

Q8

a) _____

b) _____

c) _____

9 Sir Edmund Hillary was the first man to conquer Mount Everest. Why do
   you think the author mentions the fact that Sir Edmund Hillary wrote the
   foreword to Helen's book?   *(1 mark)*

Q9

_____

_____

10 Why was Helen Thayer at a disadvantage as the only explorer to the
   magnetic North Pole that year?   *(1 mark)*

Q1C

_____

_____

_____

Section 2

These questions are about the text "Roald Amundsen" on page 7 of the Set B Reading Booklet.

11 What caused Amundsen to head for the South Pole?   *(1 mark)*   Q11

_____

_____

_____

12 Why do you think Amundsen's plans were kept secret?   *(1 mark)*   Q12

_____

_____

_____

13 Give two possible reasons why Amundsen chose a different
route to Scott.   *(2 marks)*   Q13

_____

_____

_____

_____

_____

14 Roald Amundsen's achievement was greater than that of Scott or Helen Thayer.

Do you agree with this opinion?
Explain your own opinion fully, using the texts to help you.   *(3 marks)*

_____

_____

_____

_____

_____

_____

Section 3

These questions are about the text "Scott of the Antarctic"
on pages 8 and 9 of the Set B Reading Booklet.

15 Give two possible reasons, supported by information from the text, for Scott taking longer than Amundsen to reach the Pole.

a) *(1 mark)*

Q15a

_____

_____

b) *(1 mark)*

Q15b

_____

_____

16 What in the text indicates that Scott probably expected to die? *(1 mark)*

Q16

_____

_____

17 Why do you think that Scott declared of the Pole,
"Great God! This is an awful place"? *(2 marks)*

Q17

_____

_____

_____

_____

Turn over

subtotal

18 Several items are mentioned in the text about Captain Scott.
Match each item with its purpose.

(2 marks)

One has been done for you.

reindeer fur   evidence of expedition

diary   transport supplies

fossils   to help with research

sledges   sleeping bags

photographs   to record thoughts and feelings

19 Page 9 of the Set B Reading Booklet is clearly divided into questions and answers.

How does this layout help the reader?   *(1 mark)*

_____

_____

_____

Section 4

These questions are about the poem "Explorer" by Alan Brownjohn
on page 10 of the Set B Reading Booklet.

20 What is the cat doing when it is "practising" the snow?   *(1 mark)*   Q20

_____

_____

_____

21 In the third verse, the snow is described as "*different from anything else*".
    What makes it different for the cat?   *(2 marks)*   Q21

_____

_____

_____

_____

22 Why does the author describe the snow as "*slow and cold*"?   *(2 marks)*   Q22

_____

_____

_____

_____

Turn over

subtotal

23 *"From door to fence, from fence to gate, from gate to wall to tree, and back."*
Why do you think the poet divides this line into short sections
separated by commas?

(2 marks)

Q2

_____

_____

_____

_____

24 Explain what the difference is between the snow in the garden at
two o'clock and the snow at half past three.

(2 marks)

Q24

_____

_____

_____

_____

Section 5

These questions are about the whole Set B Reading Booklet.

25 Give two reasons why a trip to the South Pole during its winter
would be more difficult. *(2 marks)*

Q25

a) _____

_____

b) _____

_____

26 What purpose is served by the table at the end of the article "Pole to Pole"?

(1 mark)

Q26

_____

_____

27 Explain why you think that explorers such as Amundsen, Scott and Helen Thayer
have always had a fascination with the North and South Poles. *(3 marks)*

Q27

_____

_____

_____

_____

_____

_____

_____

subtotal

28 Making reference to the text, consider one advantage and two
disadvantages of a trip to each pole as opposed to the other. *(3 marks)*

	Advantage	Disadvantage
North Pole	warmer climate	
South Pole		

29 Both texts *Roald Amundsen* and *Scott of the Antarctic* provide information about the
race to be the first explorer to reach the South Pole in the early twentieth century.

Why do you think the following articles have been included? *(3 marks)*

"Pole to Pole"?

_____

_____

_____

"Polar Dream"?

_____

_____

_____

"Explorer" poem

_____

_____

_____

30 What comparisons can be made between a polar explorer and the cat in
the poem _Explorer_?

Explain your response, making reference to the text if this helps.   _(3 marks)_

_____

_____

_____

_____

_____

_____

_____

END OF TEST

TEST ADVICE

This information will not appear in an official SATs paper.
It is included here to remind you not to stop working
until you are told the 1 hour test is over.

Check your answers again if time.

DON'T JUST SIT THERE WHEN FINISHED

FINDING ONE MISTAKE CAN MEAN EXTRA MARKS.
IT MAY ONLY TAKE 1 MARK TO MOVE UP TO THE NEXT LEVEL.

DO YOUR BEST and DON'T PANIC.

Reading Guide for Children

This information will not appear at the back of an official SATs Reading Test Booklet. It is included here to help you to improve your Reading Test score.

Before the test

Make sure you read a variety of good quality fiction and non-fiction texts (these will also help to give you ideas of different styles for your Writing Paper).

Get into the habit of reading each day.

Even if you are a good reader, read with an adult whenever you can and ask the adult to ask you lots of questions about the text. Both you and an adult can familiarise yourself with the Assessment Focuses on which you will be tested (see the Mark Scheme in this pack).

Work through practice papers (like the ones in this pack) to get used to the timing of the test and the question types.

Make up and answer your own questions about a text – really try to understand the characters, the story (or the subject) and why the author has written in a particular style (again use the Assessment Focus information to help you).

During the test

Read through the Reading Booklet very carefully.

When reading through the Reading Booklet, underline the important information in the text. Use brief notes or your own code for highlighting main characters, key facts, main parts of the text and changes in scene or subject.

Ensure   you always read each question very carefully.

Always   refer back to the text for relevant information.

Complete   each question – don't miss any out. No answer – NO MARK!

Notes for parents are included at the back of the Set A Reading Test Booklet (page 14).